# MARK BRAKE'S
# SPACE, TIME,
# MACHINE, MONSTER

The right of Mark Brake to be identified as the
Author of the Work has been asserted by him in accordance
with the Copyright, Designs and Patents Act 1988.

Copyright © Mark Brake 2014

Published by
Candy Jar Books
113-116 Bute Street,
Cardiff Bay, CF10 5EQ
www.candyjarbooks.co.uk

A catalogue record of this book is available
from the British Library

ISBN: 978-0-9928607-7-6

Printed and bound in the UK by
CPI Antony Rowe, Chippenham, Wiltshire, UK

Cover and illustrations: Terry Cooper
Edited by Hayley Cox, Richard Kelly,
William Rees & Shaun Russell

*This book is dedicated to Zap!*
*The author wishes to thank Ralph and Tom Pompeus, and Lorenzo*
*Sintes for their freely-given and nerdy knowledge!*

# CONTENTS

# INTRODUCTION: GEEK POWER

I've always been a geek. And I've always been obsessed with the future.

I used to read tons of futuristic sci-fi stories when I was young. Stuff about space, stuff about time travel, stuff about gadgets and inventions, stuff about superpowers that we might one day have.

You should never doubt the huge influence of comic books, graphic novels, and video games. The influence they have today. The influence they had yesterday: on me, on my friends, on everyone!

When I was a kid growing up in South Wales, I had a mate called Dai Bando. OK, his name might not have been **EXACTLY** that, but I'm protecting the innocent and making sure I don't get sued. Let's just say that 'Dai Bando' had an immensely fertile imagination.

Dai's imagination was fed and fuelled by comic books of the *Superman*, *Batman*, and *Fantastic Four* variety. The two of us had really deep conversations, even at a young age in primary school. He could have been a professor, no doubt. But he ended up working in a supermarket, and I think I know why.

This is a true story about what Dai did to me and another mate, 'Reggie Latchum': he told us we could become superheroes. How would we achieve such superhero status? Simply by "necking [that's local slang for drinking] some Super-Serum" made by Dai's own fair hand.

I know, I know. 'Reggie' and I must have been sweetly innocent (or stupid) to believe this fable and fabric of nonsense, straight out of the comic books, channeled through Dai's imagination and back out into the 'real' world.

We waited and waited for the big day when our transformation would come: from boy into Super Boy. We got impatient: *"But, Dai, when are we going to become superheroes?"* we justifiably asked. *"Don't worry about that, boys, I've got it covered: I'm making some Super-Serum in my dad's house."*

Yes. Super-Serum. In his dad's house. On an estate in South Wales, back in 1966.

It would have been wise to question the validity of Dai's claims, but we were far too distracted by his promise of all the trappings superherodom would bring: jumping over buildings, stopping speeding bullets, and of course, the girls.

But we got tired of waiting.

Dai kept on promising and promising, but nothing was delivered. In the end, we simply demanded the Super-Serum. At once. With no delay. **NOW!** We followed Dai home and impatiently waited outside his house until he 'brought forth' the Super-Serum (in comics, an inventor always seems to 'bring forth' the invention).

As Dai triumphantly came out of the lab (his dad's house), our breath was fully bated. What was he carrying, I hear you wonder. A sleek test-tube full of some fluorescent and clearly cosmic Super-Serum? A wizard potion in a cool Professor Snape-ish phial? A huge syringe with which to transform us forever? No, dear geek, Dai came out of his house with nothing more than a bowl full of ordinary water.

Gutted. In fact, mega-gutted.

Next, picture this: me and 'Reggie Latchum' in a towering Hulk-like rage reaching almost superhero proportions WITHOUT the need for a Super-Serum. After all that waiting, we were severely disappointed. We were incensed. We were INCANDESCENT! We hurled the bowl of water over Dai's head and stormed off into the sunset, disillusioned but determined to find a brighter future.

## "IT'S SCI-FI!"

Maybe my Super-Serum experience is the reason why today I get a huge buzz when I hear that one of the predictions I read about as a kid has ACTUALLY turned out to be true. And if you've lived the dream from the start and see the idea turn into reality, it can be simply inspiring.

For example, I was recently blown away by the fact that, while sitting in a 'greasy caf', I was able to watch a live soccer match on my phone. I was suitably enthusiastic to my children: *"Look, kids, I'm watching the football! It's the future! It's sci-fi!"* I said. My kids were totally unimpressed: *"No Dad, it's just a smartphone."*

But, years before that, I'd already got my satisfaction. When I became professor of science at a university, I invented study courses that focused on the future. One course was all about the search for alien life in space. Another was all about the links between science and sci-fi. But the thing they had in common was our future, on Earth and in space.

So it's no surprise that this book is about the future. It's about the ways that, in the past, we IMAGINED the future. And it's about the weird ways in which our imaginings have often come true.

This book is also based on a cool idea – we live in a science fiction world!

OK, maybe that's pretty hard to believe these days when your computer still isn't doing your homework for you, and the family android still isn't putting out the trash!

But think about the world outside your window.

As we switch on the TV, we see the latest groundbreaking discoveries: robots, face transplants, invisibility cloaks – that kind of thing. For the first time in history, we're finding planets outside of our solar system. And back on Earth scientists say the first human to live for a thousand years has already been born. It could be you. Just imagine how messy your bedroom will get by the time you're 200!

Our futuristic world was imagined long ago. Imagined in the minds of movie directors and the writers of fantastic sci-fi. And now it's the world we live in.

But there's a downside to science fiction – it's not all space tourism and hovering skateboards. The changing environment and growing population were imagined in science fiction too.

Science fiction has always helped us think about the future. And it can STILL help us do so. It can help us choose between the dizzying display of possible futures that lie ahead.

We're still making loads of science fiction. It's everywhere: in comics and books, on TV and in movies, and on every video platform known to gamers.

Of the fifty biggest-selling movies of all time, over half are science fiction films. Audiences of all ages will pay a tenner each to watch the latest science fiction blockbuster on the big screen. Eight million viewers tune in to the BBC to watch *Doctor Who*. And in the ever-expanding world of computer games, science fiction titles rule!

## WHEN DID IT ALL BEGIN?

When I was a professor of science, I did some work writing for NASA, organizing speaking tours for Russian cosmonauts, pioneers of space travel. Through this work I found that humans have been making up science fiction stories for hundreds of years.

The earliest stories were space voyages. *They're* in this book. They come from a time, the 1600s, when astronomers found out that the Earth was in orbit round the Sun, and not the other way around. Ships had started voyaging around the globe. So, writers had already started to imagine sailing out into space, four hundred years ago!

Since then there have been thousands of amazing science fiction stories – stories about aliens and time machines, spaceships and cyborgs, androids and the end of the world. Listen, all the stories have one thing in common. It's this: they're about the way science may affect our lives in the future.

# HOW TO USE THIS BOOK

This book looks at science fiction in bite-size chunks. True, there are thousands of astounding stories. But they can all be sorted into four types: **SPACE, TIME, MACHINE** and **MONSTER**.

So we've divided the book up into these four sections. It's simple, and it works!

Each of these four sections is jam-packed full of examples of how science fiction has shaped the world in which we live. The way we see and do things, the way we dream of things to come. And the way in which science has forced us to explore our future together on this little planet.

# THE TRUTH IS OUT THERE...

**W**e're all familiar with the idea of space; it's the 'final frontier' in *Star Trek*, it's where 'no one can hear you scream' in *Alien*, and it's where the Doctor hurtles his TARDIS into.

As we can see from these three famous examples, the sci-fi of space is all about the natural world.

As humans have always had an urge to explore, space stories are often about exploration and discovery in the vastness of deep space, like *Star Trek* and *Star Wars* with their legions of sleek spaceships.

At other times, space is scary. It's vast. It's very cold. And it's an unsympathetic theatre in which weird things can happen. That's the kind of mysterious space that features in *Alien*. The endless dark of space reminds us that life is delicate, in a Universe that is mostly deserted.

And in *Doctor Who* aliens often pop up in monstrous forms. They are a 'MENACE FROM SPACE'. Or agents of the scary and mysterious deep – just like the oceans in the days of the pirates. After all, you also sail through space in ships.

The alien is one of science fiction's greatest inventions.

Aliens are in our space section, rather than in monster, for two reasons. First up, sci-fi often portrays the alien, like the Martian, as a creature that lurks out there and may attack at any moment, even if you think you're safe at home. Secondly, our monster section is about humans – about the monster within us.

A lot of space stories are about the longing to escape the

limits of being human. Earth is our prison. That's why we get tales in which, often through the marvels of space travel, the wonders and terrors of the Universe are explored. They bring news of contact with alien intelligence and bug-eyed monsters.

In this way space shows how similar science fiction and science are. Sci-fi is a way of doing a kind of science: the exploration of imagined worlds.

Boffins build models of imagined worlds and then test their theories. Albert Einstein was good at this. His thought experiments led to his famous relativity theories, which caused a big revolution in ideas.

The sci-fi writer also explores imagined worlds but with more freedom. Boffins are supposed to stay within the rules of science. Science fiction has no such rules. But asking **'WHAT IF?'** questions can be common to both science and sci-fi.

There are many examples where science fiction has come up with theories far too imaginative for the science of the day, but which have later proved to be true. The theme of space contains some great examples: space travel, satellites, and men on the Moon, to name just three. But remember that the ideas of sci-fi are more important than the details; it's the sense of wonder and adventure we get that's important, and how it opens up our minds to the science possibilities.

One of the best examples of how science and science

fiction work is the question of life beyond our planet Earth.

Through its history, sci-fi has almost always believed in the alien. After all, a story in which travellers find no aliens would be very dull indeed.

So when science itself began to think about alien life, it couldn't help but be influenced by sci-fi. The sheer number of stars and orbiting planets was enough to convince most boffins that life lays waiting in the vastness of deep space. Sci-fi's influence on the alien was so great that by the end of the twentieth century, billions of real dollars had been spent in the serious search for the alien.

But, if you think about it, no real evidence of aliens has been found. Extraordinary claims about extraterrestrials require extraordinary evidence. And, so far, boffins don't have any!

## WE MAY, AFTER ALL, BE ALONE IN THE UNIVERSE ...

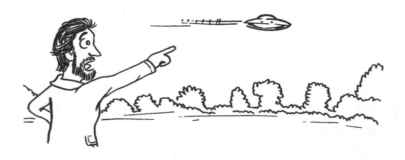

# ALIEN CONTACT

**T**hink about all those alien movies you've seen, like *ET*, *Star Wars* and *Men in Black*. Cinema seems so certain aliens are out there that we might expect them to barge into our bedrooms at any moment!

But on second thoughts, when you realise just how **HUGE** space and time actually *are*, then it begins to dawn that aliens could have beamed down to planet Earth long, long ago. Maybe their gleaming spaceships plunged into the swamp muck of a steaming coal forest. Perhaps the only creatures there to greet the aliens were hissing dinosaurs, dumb to the significance of the visit.

If Charles Darwin was right, and evolution happens on ALL planets, how do humans measure up? Who's the most evolved, them or us? Are aliens smart or stupid, nerdy or nasty?

One of the most famous alien invasion stories from science fiction is *The War of the Worlds*, by British author HG Wells. At the very start of his Martian invasion story, HG Wells asks: "But who shall dwell in these worlds if they be inhabited? Are we, or they, Lords of the World?" In other words, who's the boss of space, us or the Martians?!

HG Wells' story was very influential. Written in 1898, it was the first ever alien invasion from space. And it was the first story about a smart and superior alien intelligence that had better gadgets than we did. But *War of the Worlds* is also HG Wells' idea of what we humans may one day become. The smart Martians have evolved their brains at the expense of their bodies. Like the Daleks in *Doctor Who*, they are weedy little guys who just don't play enough sport! But there's a catch in the story. Even though the nasty and nerdy Martians are highly evolved and have the best spaceships, it was a common earthly microbe that killed them off in the end. Evolution is full of surprises.

After HG Wells' story, the meeting of humans and aliens became a twentieth-century obsession. Are we alone in the Universe? And if not, how do we measure up?

Story after story, decade after decade, portrayed aliens as smarter than us. The message seemed clear: we used to think man was the measure of all things, but when we meet our masters in space, we are in for a wake-up call!

## THINK ABOUT E.T. IF HE'S NOT SMART AND NERDY, THEN WHO IS?!

In light of all these influential stories, scientists began searching for the alien in real life. By the swinging 1960s experts began using the largest radio telescopes on Earth to beam radio messages out into space, in the hope that ET may be listening.

So many stories have been written about aliens that hardly anyone seems to stop and think that we may actually be alone in the universe. In the words of one famous science fiction writer, Arthur C. Clarke:

*"The idea that we are the only intelligent creatures in a cosmos of a hundred billion galaxies is so preposterous that there are very few astronomers today who would take it seriously. It is safest to assume, therefore, that THEY are out there and to consider the manner in which this fact may impinge upon human society."*

So you see, fiction invented the alien and science followed suit. It is astonishing that millions of dollars have been spent on serious scientific missions to search for intelligent aliens, as no evidence has ever been found that they exist!

# SPACE TRAVEL

**F**ancy a ride on the Death Star?

Maybe take a trip into space, kick back on a space station, or slip slowly from blue sky up into black on a space elevator. Space elevator? **SERIOUSLY?!**

Many people have dreamed of going into space, but only a few hundred proper astronauts have so far made the trip. That may soon change. Companies are now planning space tourism projects, as long as you have the money to pay for the flight.

Sci-fi writers have dreamed of the age of space travel for many decades. Arthur C Clarke imagined businesses working on the Moon in *A Fall of Moondust* (1961). And film director Stanley Kubrick worked with Clarke on the famous 1968 movie *2001: A Space Odyssey*, in which space tourists are served drinks by a stewardess in a station orbiting the Earth. It all looks so very civilized.

The possibility of space tourism got a lot closer in 2004 with the Ansari X-Prize. This was a competition to design a re-usable way of taking people into space, getting them back to Earth, and re-launching again within two weeks. The prize was won. The technology is within reach. And now companies are developing flights into space for the early 21st century.

Of course, there's nowhere to actually *GO*. At least not until a tourist space station is built, such as the one in *2001*. For now, passengers will be taken just above the 100km barrier that separates Earth from space, and then they will be brought back home.

Yet companies are also dreaming up space stations in orbit about the Earth.

Bigelow Aerospace is working on the idea of an inflatable space hotel. Imagine taking a dip in a space station swimming pool with a glass bottom, through which you can see the Earth below. Orbital stations can be made to spin, which makes a kind of gravity that grounds those inside. Stations would get the same sunlight as the Earth and can be built with dome sections where food could be grown. These space cities could house hundreds or even thousands of people in the future. Maybe eventually some people will actually live in space, and one of them could be you – better start packing.

## BUT WHAT ABOUT THAT SPACE ELEVATOR?

If space stations become a reality, we'll need a cheap and regular way of getting back and fore, right? A way that doesn't use up too much rocket fuel and is kind to the environment. That's where the space elevator comes in. Imagine jumping into an elevator and pressing the button marked 'space' or even 'space station'. Such a thing was imagined in an 1895 book called *Daydreams of Heaven and Earth*, by Russian rocket pioneer Konstantin Tsiolkovsky.

At heart, the design of a space elevator is a 47,000 kilometre cable made from an as yet undeveloped material. This 'beanstalk' material would need to be thirty times stronger than steel and have a diameter of no more than ten centimetres.

TRICKY.

This super-strength beanstalk stuff would be tethered to the space station to enable continuous transport into space.

NASA has spent millions of dollars running a competition to design space elevators, yet up until now the elevator idea has failed to capture the public imagination. So come on, space cadets, get those thinking caps on. How do we sell this space elevator idea to the world?

Let's get them all to realize the cosmic power behind that elevator button marked 'space'!

# SPACE FLIGHT

The spaceship was first imagined when Shakespeare was still alive.

Incredibly, when astronomer Galileo first clapped his telescopic eyes on the craters of our craggy Moon, excited maths boffin, Johannes Kepler, wrote to Galileo. This is what he said (kind of):

*"Hey, Galileo, big up the scope! Once we've mastered the art of flight, Gal, let's create ships with sails for space travel, and let's make maps for the brave sky-travellers of the future."*

And this letter of Kepler's was written in 1610! Isn't it marvellous to think that these creative fellas thought about space travel and space ships over 350 years before man landed on the Moon?! That's the power of the imagination.

It's one thing imagining yourself sailing away into space. But it's quite another dreaming up a way of actually *getting there*.

People have been pondering this for much longer than you think. Take the writer Lucian, for example, who lived long ago and wrote a book called *True History* in about

160AD. The book is a space voyage, but Lucian's preferred way of propelling his adventurers into space was by using a giant waterspout, which pushed them into the air so powerfully that they ended up in space.

Waterspouts seem a bit random, so the next effort was a little easier to steer. The Bishop of Llandaff, Francis Godwin, had his book *The Man in the Moon* published in 1638. And you'll never guess his method of getting to the Moon: *geese*.

Yep, that's right – old goosey goosey gander. The Moon voyager in the story harnesses himself to around three-dozen geese, which carry him higher and higher. He doesn't actually mean to end up on the Moon but remembers that the geese migrate each year to the Moon to hibernate (yeah, right), and so it is to the Moon they carry him.

If geese are not to your liking, there's always dew.

This ingenious method of propulsion was invented by romantic French hero Cyrano de Bergerac. His reasoning went something like this: dew droplets can be seen first thing in the morning, but when sunlight shines on them, they evaporate, rising into the air. So the hero in Cyrano's story collects as many dew droplets as he can, bottles them, and securely fastens the bottles around his waist. When he then stands in the morning sunlight, hey presto, the evaporating dew lifts him to the Moon! And all this in the mid 1600s.

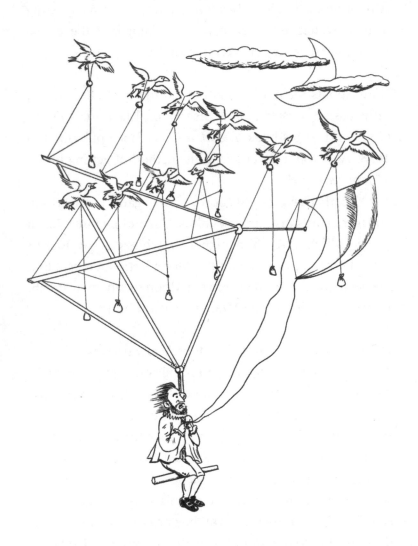

Some of the early space travel stories assumed that the atmosphere of the Earth extended all the way up to the Moon. When boffins found it didn't, they had to put their thinking caps back on. The most famous Moon travel story, before the obsession with the rocket, is the 1865 story *From the Earth to the Moon* by Jules Verne.

In Verne's book the basic modern ideas of space travel are in place. The vacuum of space is respected. The lack of atmosphere is recognized. And a sealed capsule is used to take the astronauts into orbit. The only difference is they are shot out of a huge gun! But when you come to think about it, that's very similar to a rocket.

Since then the idea of space travel has become very popular. Yet by 2007 fewer than 500 people had travelled beyond the Karman Line, which is 100km above the Earth's sea level. All that looks about to change, though, with the increasing interest in space tourism. Who knows, you could even end up reading this book in Earth's orbit!

# SPACE SATELLITES

**T**ry a Google image search on 'space satellite'. Go on. Do it.

## WHAT DO YOU FIND?

- A host of romantic images of single satellites wheeling their lonely way in orbit about an unpolluted planet Earth?
- Or a dense forest of satellites that you can barely spot the Earth below.

## WHICH IS THE MOST REALISTIC PICTURE?

Satellites are the main way that mobile phones and pagers communicate with each other. And just think how many of *those* there are on the Earth. Satellites are also used for monitoring climate, directing SatNavs and providing television signals. So it stands to reason that by now there'd be lots of satellites in space. Where did it all begin? **SCIENCE FICTION.**

The most familiar satellite to grace our night sky is the

Moon. It's Earth's natural satellite. When the first mention of an artificial satellite occurred, it was referred to as a 'brick moon', in other words a satellite that is made by man, rather than naturally occurring. *Brick Moon* is the name of a story written by Edward Everett Hale in 1861. It wasn't long before famous French sci-fi writer Jules Verne was also imagining satellites in his 1878 story *The Begum's Millions*. In this book a projectile is shot from a huge cannon with so much force that it enters Earth's orbit. One of the characters in the story writes a letter:

*"...we saw your perfect shell, at forty-five minutes and four seconds past eleven, pass above our town. It was flying towards the west, circulating in space, which it will continue to do until the end of time."*

The **'OUTSIDE THE BOX'** way of thinking, which science fiction has used for so long, was a huge influence on the design and making of satellites. In fact, the type of satellites that now encircle the globe were imagined by sci-fi writer Arthur C Clarke, in a short technical paper in *Wireless World* in 1954. By 1955 the USA announced that it planned to put satellites in space, giving themselves a target of 1958, but the USSR responded by saying that by the end of 1957 they would launch a Soviet satellite.

## THE SPACE RACE HAD BEGUN.

The Soviets were true to their word. Sputnik One was indeed launched into orbit on 4th October 1957. It was quickly followed a month later by Sputnik Two. This second Soviet satellite was also known as 'Muttnik'. That's because it featured Laika the space dog, not just the first living creature launched into space, but also the first space casualty, when she didn't return safely. ☹

Since those early days of exploration, the dark skies above the Earth have become populated with all sorts of satellites. A recent survey suggests that only 7% of the thousands that are now in orbit are actually active. The others are debris destined to continue their journey around the globe or maybe something more dramatic.

# GOOGLE EARTH

One of the World Wide Web's most popular programs is **GOOGLE EARTH**, launched in 2005. As you probably know, Google Earth (like NASA's 2004 World Wind) combines maps, satellite images, and aerial photos to make a virtual globe. It's a computer simulation of planet Earth. And it has a science fiction origin.

Virtual globes first appeared in fiction in 1992, in the book *Snowcrash* by Neal Stephenson. *Snowcrash* features a program developed by the Central Intelligence Corporation, simply called Earth. The Earth program allows the user to navigate about the planet, swooping down to any detail you wish to see, even at street level.

Virtual globes also made an early appearance in the movies. In the 1998 sci-fi thriller *Enemy of the State* starring Will Smith, we saw computer simulations similar to a real-time virtual globe, which allowed the American security services to hunt down our hero.

*Star Trek: The Next Generation* went one step further. The series created virtual universes allowing virtual characters to live out virtual lives, whilst being monitored from the real world. And back in the real world, Google Earth's chief boffin has admitted being inspired by the mapping capability of Star Trek's tricoder.

# A CASE OF SCIENCE FICTION
# LEADING THE WAY!

# MOON MEN

**E**ver gazed up at the silvery Moon and wondered what it might be like to live up there?

Our ancestors did.

Two thousand years ago a Greek writer named Lucian dreamt up a story about life on the Moon. He imagined all kinds of strange creatures, such as cloud centaurs, stalk-and-mushroom men, and even acorn-dogs! Lucian's Moon-men characters used a well and a mirror to act as a telescope, so they could watch people on Earth below!

It wasn't until one and a half thousand years later that Italian astronomer Galileo actually invented a **REAL** telescope. Galileo's telescope didn't use a well and a mirror, but it did use a glass lens. In 1610 he urged people who heard of his new telescopic discovery to imagine walking on the lunar mountains and craters, just like on Earth.

For the first time the Moon came alive. It became a real object for the great majority of people, and not just a flat disc in the sky. True, it had been imagined long ago in Greek fiction by Lucian and others, but with Galileo's telescope the Moon became an object of wonder, as more and more people began to ask: Is life dwelling there? May we one day walk over that craggy terrain? What would it be like to race a quad bike inside a giant crater?! (OK, maybe not that last question!)

Now, new stories emerged of what life might be like on the Moon.

A German maths genius called Johannes Kepler imagined a journey to our natural satellite (indeed, using the word satellite for the Moon was actually invented by Kepler). Kepler's Moon book was called *Somnium*, and it came out in 1634. It was the first Moon-voyage story with a strong scientific flavour. In his book Kepler imagined alien life fit for a lunar landscape. Strange Moon serpents stalked his story and life on the Moon was hard, as you can imagine!

Another new Moon story was a book called *The Man in the Moone*. It was written by Francis Godwin, the Bishop of Llandaff in Cardiff, and was extraordinary for being the first English book in history to portray alien contact.

The aliens in question, of course, were the Moon people. *The Man in the Moone* captured the imagination of John Wilkins, who was First Secretary of the Royal Society in

London, the world's oldest society of practicing boffins which is still in existence. Inspired by Godwin's book, John Wilkins proposed a flying machine that would one day wing its way moonwards. Yes, the idea of space travel really is **THAT** old!

Centuries later, fact followed fiction as astronauts from the West and cosmonauts from the East raced to be the first Earth society to land a man on the Moon. Apollo got there first. And a dozen US astronauts from the various missions were the only humans to set foot on lunar soil.

They found that the Moon was dead.

And yet, at just over a mere light second away, the Moon had been conquered and claimed for science – just as predicted in those science fiction stories of old. The Moon remains as a stepping-stone for the future development of the Solar System at large. After all, once we've conquered the Moon, and then Mars, where else is there to go but to **"INFINITY AND BEYOND!"**

# OTHER UNIVERSES

Is this the best of all possible worlds?

How come there's no robot to do your homework, no droid to dress you when you're comatose on a school morning? And, dude, where's your flying car?!

Writers and thinkers have always wondered whether there may be worlds other than this one, but the most famous version of the question was first lit in the nervous system of German philosopher Gottfried Leibniz. Now, Leibniz was trying to solve the problem of evil. His thinking went something like this: if God is good and all-powerful, how come there is so much suffering and injustice in the world? It's a fair question.

What was Leibniz's answer? His reply went something like this: God is a kind of fixer, a betting man, and He simply chose from a host of all original possibilities to make the world we live in. And since God is good, this world must be the best of all possible worlds. HMMM!

Science soon came up with its own questions about other worlds and other universes.

The idea that our Universe is merely one of many is a part of the 'many-worlds interpretation' of a branch of science called quantum theory. This theory imagines an infinite number of parallel universes making up a 'multiverse' that together compose all of physical reality.

Not only that, but such a multiverse contains all possible Earthly histories and all possible physical universes. Head hurting? Don't worry, it's natural. In fact, quantum eggheads are often saying that if you are not completely confused by quantum theory, you do not understand it!

In science fiction and fantasy stories, such parallel universes may also be called 'other dimensions', 'alternate universes', 'quantum universes', 'parallel worlds', or even 'alternate realities'. Indeed, the idea that other worlds lie in parallel to ours is one of the oldest in fantastic fiction.

In modern times most writers were slow to realise the potential extravagance in all this. The most distinguished exception, of course, is Lewis Carroll's 1865 story *Alice's Adventures in Wonderland* in which Alice pops through a rabbit hole into an alternate reality that's peopled by strange creatures, weird playing cards, and mythic beasts.

In *The Lion, the Witch and the Wardrobe* there are two parallel worlds: ours and Narnia. And in *His Dark Materials*, by Phillip Pullman, Lyra and Will are able to travel amongst many worlds by using a subtle knife to cut their way through the fabric of space and time!

Phillip Jose Farmer's story *Sail On! Sail On!* describes an alternate 1492 AD where the Earth is actually flat. The nature of this other-world is such that Columbus sails over the edge of the world into Earth orbit, never to return from his mission. **SIMPLY BRILLIANT!**

*Doctor Who* often has stories with parallel universes as plotlines. In one such episode, the Doctor travels to a parallel UK which is ruled by a fascist leader, like Hitler. Thankfully, this parallel world is destroyed by a volcano. Some people get all the luck!

And who can forget the movie ending of *Men in Black* (1997). The final sequence reveals our Universe held in a container resembling a marble. An alien hand picks up the 'marble' and pops it into a bag full of universe-marbles.

Some eggheads today believe that quantum universes could actually exist. In a 2003 issue of *Scientific American*, they suggested that our Milky Way Galaxy has a twin, in which there is a twin Earth, which in turn contains a twin of you!

No doubt there's also a twin of this book. Come to think of it, if the 'many-worlds interpretation' of reality is true, then in some parallel world this book will win the Rhone-Poulenc science book award. And also not win it ☹

# ANTI-MATTER

**S**cience fiction crackles with masses of anti-matter. It dreams up huge quantities of the stuff.

## WHAT'S ANTI-MATTER?

Anti-matter is made of stuff that's opposite to ordinary matter. The idea was first mooted by English boffin Paul Dirac in 1930. The existence of the first antimatter particle, the positron (or anti-electron), was confirmed two years later.

Scotty, the Chief Engineer in *Star Trek*, uses frozen anti-hydrogen as the primary fuel for the propulsion of the *Starship Enterprise*. Boffins in Dan Brown's *Angels and Demons* manage to create enough anti-matter to blow up the Vatican (revenge for the Gunpowder Plot?). And sci-fi writers have imagined antimatter galaxies and even an entire anti-matter universe.

But anti-matter has to tread carefully in our Universe. Assuming it *could* tread, which it can't. But you get my drift. Listen: so far only trillionths of a gram of antimatter have been isolated in real labs. But the potential of antimatter is colossal. It would make a fantastic power source. Sadly, Scotty has a long way to go before he has enough to power a spaceship!

When antimatter meets ordinary matter, the result is 100% explosive mutual annihilation.

And, as Einstein showed us with his famous equation $E=mc^2$ a small amount of matter (m) is converted into an enormous amount of energy (E), as the (c) in the equation is the speed of light, a big number (300000000).

Put simply, a mass of anti-matter equivalent to a small dog could produce most of the world's electricity for one year. If you can *imagine* an anti-matter dog, that is. (Would we call it an anti-poodle? Or an anti-Yorkshire Terrier? Would it eat anti-meat and anti-dog food? And would *any* of this really anti-matter?!)

# UFOS & FLYING SAUCERS

**U**nexplained objects in the sky are nothing new.

The Biblical prophet Ezekiel is meant to have had a cosmic vision. Traditional accounts of Ezekiel's vision say that he had an encounter with God and four living creatures, or Cherubim (a type of spiritual being mentioned in the Bible).

Now, this cosmic account just wasn't cosmic enough for Josef F. Blumrich, one of the Chiefs at NASA's Marshall Space Flight Center. Blumrich suggested that Ezekiel hadn't just had a cosmic vision, but had a close encounter with aliens – ancient astronauts in a shuttlecraft from a distant planet! Just goes to show that even nerds at NASA can make mistakes.

Where was Blumrich's evidence? A mere re-interpretation of Bible scripture, tbh. Not exactly scientific. And that's the main thing to bear in mind about claims such as 'UFOs are alien spaceships'. Extraordinary claims need extraordinary evidence, and if you ain't got the evidence, why should people believe you?

Mystery airships, or phantom airships, were a class of UFO reported over the western United States, and spread east, during 1896 and 1897. Typical reports mentioned unidentified lights and beings that looked like humans, though sometimes the beings claimed to be from Mars (which was then commonly believed to have intelligent life on its surface).

The sightings of the mystery airships are typical of UFO reports; people always tend to see only the believable technology of the day. For example, no one in the late 1800s ever saw an alien with an iPod!

The phrase 'flying saucer' was first coined by US businessman Kenneth Arnold on seeing nine discs flying in formation in Washington State in 1947. Arnold's sighting is often thought of as the birth of the modern UFO age, which ran for about twenty years until the late 1960s.

## 1947 WAS A BIG YEAR FOR UFOS!

It was also the year of the infamous Roswell Incident, which focused on claims that a flying saucer had crash-landed in the New Mexico desert. One year earlier American science fiction writer Theodore Sturgeon had penned a short story, *Mewhu's Jet*, with striking similarities to the Roswell Incident. And time after time in the decades before Roswell, science fiction had presented the spaceship as cutting edge technology.

All these modern UFO sightings happened at a time known as the Cold War, when relations between West and East, and particularly the United States and the Soviet Union (or Russia, as it's now known), were a bit frosty. Both sides were busy inventing secret weapons that they didn't want the other side to know about. So it's likely that the American Press helped people come to the conclusion that extraterrestrials were flying saucers, rather than let folk realize it was probably the American military testing out their latest weapon technology. It's no wonder that at the height of the Saucer Craze of the 1950s and early '60s, people came to the crazy conclusion of the 'ET hypothesis': that flying saucers were piloted by aliens from another planet!

# OTHER WORLDS

**E**ver clapped eyes on another planet? No? You may be wrong, you know.

Five of the planets in our own Solar System (Mercury, Venus, Mars, Jupiter, and Saturn) are visible to the naked eye and always have been. You may have gazed up at one of these nearby planets, thinking it was a star. For many centuries Venus was known as the Morning Star, until stargazers realized their mistake. Our ancestors made an obsessive study of the planets and no doubt wondered whether there was life on their surfaces (OK, Jupiter and Saturn don't have surfaces as such, but you get my drift!).

In the late 1800s it became popular to believe that there was life on Mars. As Mars is the closest planet to Earth – the surface of which we can see through a telescope – eggheads speculated about Martians in fiction and fact. One chap, an American named Percival Lowell, was so convinced of life on Mars that he wrote an entire book describing how the parched Martians used a canal system to bring water down from Mars' polar caps to the regions on its equator. OUCH!

## IMAGINE BEING *THAT* WRONG!

Venus also came in for a fictional makeover. In real life Venus is completely covered in cloud, so if there WERE any Venusians you wouldn't see them anyway. That didn't stop boffins speculating. In the early 20th century a Swedish scientist called Svante Arrhenius declared that the surface of Venus was covered in swamps, and he compared the planet to the tropical rain forests of the African Congo!

When we Earthlings began to send rockets and probes to other planets in our Solar System, it became clear that worlds like Venus were hostile to life, so the idea of fictional planets became far more popular in space stories.

In *Doctor Who* the Doctor comes from the fictional planet of Gallifrey. Superman is an alien who was born, with the name Kal-El, on the planet of Krypton, and in the *Thor* films Asgard is one of the Nine Worlds ruled by Thor's dad, Odin.

With so many fictional planets in our creative stories, scientists began to wonder whether we'd ever find any real worlds like our own.

After all, people realized space was so big, and the stars

and planets so numerous, that there was enough land in the sky to give every human his or her own private Earth-sized world. Having your own planet – how cool would that be?! Might take a bit of maintenance, though. You know what tidying your room's like, imagine having to tidy your planet.

The search for other planets ended in 1995. That was when astronomers began to find clear evidence of the first exoplanets – planets outside our Solar System. These exoplanets are found orbiting stars such as 47 Ursa Major, 51 Pegasi, and 16 Cygni, all visible to the naked eye and relatively close to home.

At first, it was understood that many of these exoplanets were more like Jupiter, but it was only a matter of time before we discovered another Earth. In 2007 astronomers reported a planet 20 light-years away in the constellation Libra. Orbiting the faint star Gliese 581 and with a radius 1.5 times our own planet's, this new world was dubbed 'super-Earth'.

Today, we live in a great age of discovery. A European team of scientists has recently come up with an amazing estimate: they think that perhaps 40% of the estimated 160 billion red dwarf stars in our Milky Way Galaxy have a 'super-Earth'. And these 'super-Earths' would be orbiting at a distance from their parent star that would allow water to flow freely on their surface.

# THIS COULD MEAN LIFE – ALIEN LIFE!

# FORCE FIELDS

**A**ll matter is made of atoms. Atoms are bound together by forces. Now take away the atoms but leave the forces behind. That's a force field.

Well, let's be clear, that's a force field in science fiction. It's a concept we all know and love. It's what happens when satellite shrapnel, rogue drones, or Darth Vader's newly severed limb wings your way. Just knock up a force field and put your feet up. **JOB DONE**.

The first force field found its way into fiction with the *Skylark* and *Lensman* books by EE 'Doc' Smith in the 1930s and '40s. A more modern version is the 'deflector' on the USS Enterprise in *Star Trek*.

In truth, force fields are trickier. As yet there is no known force capable of repelling all objects and energies. But boffins are working on it. That is, after all, what boffins do.

Scientists at NASA's *Kennedy Space Centre* and the *NASA Institute for Advanced Concepts* are researching the possibility of electric shields for Moon bases. Most of the deadly radiation in space is made up of electrically charged particles. So, why not use a powerful electric field that has the same charge as the incoming radiation, thus repelling the radiation away?

Now that's a force field.

# TOP 10 ALIENS

## I  The Doctor

*Claim to fame: what do you mean claim to fame? He's the Doctor!*

**ALIEN FACTOIDS:** a humanoid Time Lord from the planet Gallifrey who's able to navigate through time and space using an internally vast time machine called the TARDIS. Be honest, that already sounds like unbeatable credentials! He famously has two hearts, a mega intellect, is able to go without air, is telepathic, and occasionally shows a superhero level of stamina. And on the topic of superheroes…

## 2  Superman

*Claim to fame: erm, he's Superman!?*

**ALIEN FACTOIDS:** OK, OK, I know elsewhere in this book Kryptonians are listed among the most ridiculous aliens, but this particular Kryptonian, Kal-El, just happens to be one of the greatest cultural icons ever. His arsenal of powers includes flight, faster-than-light speed, an array of super-vision powers, and super-intelligence. In fact, all the things that we humans have, except in a 'super' variety. Apart from the flying. Oh, and the x-ray vision. Oh, and the... [author continues to mumble list to himself, disproving his own theory].

# 3 The Xenomorph

*Claim to fame: the ultimate killing machine, from the* Alien *franchise*

**ALIEN FACTOIDS:** we first see the Xenomorph when it bursts out from the throbbing chest of actor John Hurt (who's also played the Doctor!) during dinner. For the rest of the movie, director Ridley Scott gives only the merest glimpse of the alien, so we have to piece together its fearful symmetry: snapping sets of fangs, acid for blood which corrodes all it touches, and an incredible appetite for bloody murder. Eek. RUUUUUUUNNNNNNN!

# 4 E.T.

*Claim to fame: the stranded critter from the 1982 movie* E.T.: the Extra-Terrestrial

**ALIEN FACTOIDS:** the podgy Einstein lookalike who got left behind on planet Earth has been an enduring favourite of moviegoers for many years. Apparently. They quote his big blue eyes, his telepathic ability, the fact he can make stuff float, and that weird luminous finger that hails cosmic taxis.

# 5 Aliens from the War of the Worlds

*Claim to fame: they are the first alien invasion from space, they are agents of the void*

**ALIEN FACTOIDS**: yes, HG Wells' Martians in *War of the Worlds* were the first ever aliens to invade the Earth. **RESPECT!** They may have looked pathetically weedy inside their tripod vehicles (a 3-legged walker that pre-dates the Star Wars AT-AT Walkers by 80 years) but they had heat-rays that could turn you into Victorian cinders!

# 6 Engineers

*Claim to fame: humanoid aliens from the 2012 movie* Prometheus

**ALIEN FACTOIDS**: colossal looking humanoid aliens who create man in *Prometheus.* In the beginning of the film, a sole engineer, like a dark angel, is seen sacrificing himself and his DNA to bring life to planet Earth, and us!

# 7 Prawns

*Claim to fame: the aliens from the* District 9 *movie*

**ALIEN FACTOIDS**: with perhaps a pinch of Predator, the zest of a Xenomorph, and a dash of Ood, you have the recipe for a 'Prawn', the strange creatures at the heart of District 9, who seem to have a weird liking for tinned cat food.

# 8 Worm Guys

*Claim to fame: the mischievous extraterrestrials from* Men in Black I *(1997)* II *(2002)*

ALIEN FACTOIDS: looking like some kind of weird hybrid between a meerkat and a stick insect, this motley crew of mutants are so badly behaved they seem like a forerunner of Paul.

# 9 Mr Spock

*Claim to fame: the half-Vulcan from the* Star Trek *franchise*

ALIEN FACTOIDS: OK, Spock might be half-Vulcan and half-human, but how can we possibly leave someone as famous as him out of our Top Ten? It's not logical, Captain. He's a boffin of the highest order, having served as Science Officer on the USS Enterprise. And his regular dilemmas between logic and emotion remind us, as do many aliens, what it's actually like to be human. If that makes logical sense... [author starts bawling eyes out at being misunderstood].

# 10 The Na'vi

*Claim to fame: the alien race in James Cameron's sci-fi epic* Avatar

ALIEN FACTOIDS: when the movie was first released, the

SPACE, TIME, MACHINE, MONSTER

Na'vi were known as 'smurfs on a stick'. 'Smurfs' because
they have sky-tinted skin and 'on a stick' because the film's
famous use of 3D made them stick out from the screen a
fair bit. Folk may scoff, but the Na'vi are tree-dwelling aliens
dedicated to the protection of their land and environment,
which teaches humans a welcome lesson.

# TOP 10 SPACESHIPS

## I   The TARDIS

*Claim to fame: iconic spaceship and time travel machine from* Doctor Who

**DESIGN:** it has a Chameleon circuit, of course, which means it could make itself look like anything it wants, but the circuit is unreliable and broke, **MOSTLY** fixing the TARDIS as a 1960s police telephone box.

## 2   Naboo Queen's Royal Starship

*Claim to fame: the personal royal vessel of Queen Amidala from* Star Wars

**DESIGN:** like the coolest sleek and silver spaceship in the history of the universe.

## 3   X-Wing Fighters

*Claim to fame: the Rebel Alliance's fighter of choice in* Star Wars

**DESIGN:** elegant straight lines make it look like an Earthly aeroplane, but it also has a cute cubbyhole for your R2D2

droid, so he can sit there while you go bombing about.

# 4 United Planets Cruiser C-57D

*Claim to fame: the quintessential (look it up!) saucer-ship, from* Forbidden Planet

**DESIGN:** a pretty vanilla saucer-ship in flight. On landing a central column descends from the undercarriage whilst the ship hovers on a spectacular suspensor beam.

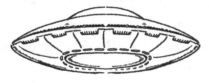

# 5 Max

*Claim to fame: the spaceship from* Flight of the Navigator

**DESIGN:** like a mirrored flying turtle, with a cute little ladder for disembarking.

# 6 Nostromo

*Claim to fame: the huge industrial star freighter from* Alien

**DESIGN:** like a tug, really, but one which hauls an enormous ore refinery which is 1.5 miles in length!

## 7 The Millennium Falcon

*Claim to fame: the spaceship from* Star Wars *piloted by Hans Solo and Chewbacca*

DESIGN: like a cosmic Alfa Romeo – looks cool, but notoriously unreliable.

## 8 The Heart of Gold

*Claim to fame: the ship from* Hitchhikers Guide to the Galaxy, *which runs on the nonsense of the Infinite Improbability Drive*

DESIGN: looks quite a lot like the shower-head in your bathroom.

## 9 Mothership

*Claim to fame: the alien spaceship from* Close Encounters of the Third Kind

DESIGN: like a firework display exploding underneath a flying saucer.

## 10 USS Enterprise

*Claim to fame: the spaceship of Captain Kirk and Mr Spock from the original* Star Trek *TV series*

DESIGN: cosmic frisbee.

# TOP 10 TAGLINES

*A tagline is a kind of catchphrase or slogan, which is used to advertise up-and-coming movies. The best ones sum up the movie in one catchy sentence, and most of the best ever movie taglines have been in sci-fi movies...*

**1**
*In space no one can hear you scream*
Alien (1979)

**2**
*Houston we have a problem*
Apollo 13 (1995)

**3**
*We are not alone*
Close Encounters of the Third Kind (1977)

**4**
*A long time ago in a galaxy far, far away*
Star Wars (1977)

**5**
*Earth. It was fun while it lasted*
Armageddon (1998)

**6**
*An adventure 65 million years in the making*
Jurassic Park (1993)

**7**
*You'll believe a man can fly!*
Superman (1978)

**8**
*Nice planet. We'll take it!*
Mars Attacks! (1996)

**9**
*Eternity is closer than you think*
Star Trek: Insurrection (1998)

**10**
*He is afraid. He is alone. He is three million light years from home*
E.T. the Extra-Terrestrial (1982)

**W**ouldn't it be great if, like the Doctor, we could tamper with time? At least a little bit. We could jump timelines, guide evolution, try re-writing history, or even cheat death.

Many moons ago, once science had caught on, it began to influence all parts of life. And boffins wanted not just to explore nature; they also wanted to exploit it. They wanted to control nature.

Boffins also began to realize that time was limitless and incredibly vast in scale. Even the stars, it was suggested, may grow old and die.

By the time of the Industrial Revolution, great machines turned over the soil of the world. The death toll of extinction rang out to us for the first time. It was only then that we began to dig up dinosaurs, and the fossil record churned out evidence of other creatures no longer found on Earth. Evolution forced us all to think about the terrible extent of history, in which all sorts of creatures come and go. Would humans one day also become extinct?

What if we could master time, that brutal agent that devours creatures, great and small? Suddenly, there was no greater challenge for science.

And so began sci-fi's obsession with time.

Time travel stories made their first appearance during the Industrial Revolution too. The ancient Greeks had two words for time: '*chronos*' and '*kairos*'. *Kairos* was a moment of time in which something special happens. *Chronos* was about measured, ordered time. Industrial society brought with it a mechanical approach to nature. *Chronos* came to the fore, and time travel was born.

HG Wells gave science fiction one of its coolest devices – the time machine. Wells' book is an ingenious voyage of discovery. *The Time Traveller* sets out to master time, but he discovers the unavoidable truth; time is lord of all. The real meaning of the story's title becomes clear: humans are trapped by the mechanism of time and bound by a history that leads to extinction. **GULP!**

But after Wells sci-fi writers continued in their attempts to master time and nail down the future for us.

Wells himself wondered what would become of man in *The War of the Worlds*. The invading Martians are not only a brutal force of evolution; they are also the 'men' of the future. They are alien, yet they are human. They are what we may one day become, with their over-developed brains and withered bodies. This is what happens when you spend too much time on game consoles and not enough time playing sport!

Time travel proved to have other uses too; it meant writers could make their readers think about history by writing *different* histories to the one that had actually happened.

A favourite topic here was a Nazi victory in World War II. How would history have looked if Hitler had won? It was a way of creating a different past and consider how that could have impacted our present and future.

A great example of this is *The Man in the High Castle*, written by Philip K Dick in 1962. The Nazis win, and Germany and Japan control the United States. But what's different about *The Man in the High Castle*, rather than telling a tale about just one history, is that some of the book's characters are aware that other histories exist! Which history is real? Which history is true?

In film and fiction it soon became common for characters to jump freely between alternative histories, with each history having its own future. That's what happens in the *Back to the Future* and *Terminator* series. In *Terminator* droid assassins are sent back from the future by a race of intelligent machines bent on the extermination of humans.

Of course, the main business of time travel stories is to entertain, but they also educate. These tales in time enable us to ask questions: How open is the future? Do we really have the ability to change things? In a sense, isn't all history a fiction written by the winners? How can we ever know anything about time other than the histories we create?

# AAARRRGGGHHH! MY BRAIN HURTS!

# COUNTDOWNS

It's not easy launching a modern rocket, you know. It's tricky enough doing an uphill start in a car, or using a twin tub washing machine (so my nan tells me). But imagine all the different things that have to be co-ordinated before a rocket launch-off can occur:

*"ROCKETS PRIMED? CHECK.*
*FINS OUT? CHECK.*
*POINTING AT THE MOON? CHECK."*

And how do you make sure that all these things happen together and at precisely the right moment?

That's exactly the question that German film director Fritz Lang pondered when he was creating his legendary 1929 movie *Frau in Mond* (*Woman in the Moon*). *Frau in Mond* tells the tale of finding gold, and love, on the Moon. Often considered to be one of the very first 'serious' sci-fi films, *Frau in Mond* was a silent movie released at a time when the talkies were beginning to make silent films outdated.

Fritz Lang's idea for getting the rocket launch-off just right was to invent the countdown.

In the final moments before the rocket ignites, images appear on the screen, showing the countdown from ten down to zero. It was an elegant but simple solution and was immediately copied by the growing space industry. The speed with which this sci-fi movie invention caught on in the real space business may also have something to do with the fact that influential rocket pioneer Hermann Oberth worked as an advisor on Fritz Lang's film.

# TELEPORTATION

**P**icture the scene…

It's a wet Wednesday afternoon and you're trapped in double French, the most tedious topic known to man.

No need to panic. We have a plan. Outside the classroom, hidden in a far corner of the school campus, sits your mate with a Teleportation Joystick. What's a Teleportation Joystick? Don't worry about that, I've just made it up, but bear with me. With this gadget your mate can teleport you, body and soul, out of double French altogether. Secretly, as the teacher's back is turned, you whisper into your wristwatch receptor, *"Beam me out, Justin!"* (Sci-fi-type prediction: in the near future your mate will change his name to something less Bieberesque.)

A shimmer of light. Your whole body disappears from the classroom of doom and magically reappears somewhere much less boring!

In the past such teleportation tales would have been mixed in with magic, and the ability to teleport would have been some kind of magical gift. A modern version of this is in the *Harry Potter* books. Here, the magical method of moving yourself from one place to another is called **APPARITION**. Wizards fix their mind on where they want to be, and they instantly reappear there. It's tricky to pull off and can be disastrous if botched up.

The first teleportation tale with science as a means of transport is the 1877 story *The Man Without a Body* by Edward Page Mitchell. In this tale the boffin hero manages to disassemble his cat, telegraph its atoms, and then reassemble the cat again. But when the boffin tries the same technique on himself, a power cut happens and he sadly only succeeds in transmitting his head. **D'OH!**

Since then sci-fi has used the idea of transferring matter from one place to another in many movies and stories.

In the 1939 serial *Buck Rogers*, teleportation was a cheap way of moving characters from place to place. The same thing was done in *Star Trek*, in the 1960s. The first plan of the *Star Trek* programme makers was to have the spaceship USS Enterprise land on a planet, but that would have cost too much money to make. So they went for the cheaper and more imaginative option of teleporting people to the planet using a transporter. Characters were beamed down with ease, but it's not always easy transferring stuff from place to place.

## CONSIDER *THE FLY...*

*The Fly* was written in 1957, and there have been three movie versions. They all tell the tale of what happens when a boffin and a fly accidentally end up fusing in a teleportation attempt. It's meant to be horror, but when you see a man with a fly's head, it really is quite funny. The fly with a man's head is even funnier.

The way all this works in fiction is simple enough: the object you want to transfer, or teleport, has to be destroyed and recreated somewhere else. Yes, you can already see the trouble ahead: what if it doesn't go smoothly? Also, if you are teleported and your original self is destroyed, is the copy of you that appears elsewhere genuine? Freaky.

Boffins have been a little slow to catch up with the sci-fi, but tbh, teleportation may not be so easy to pull off. In 2006 boffins in Denmark teleported a real object for the first time. Though it was very, very tiny, it was still made out of trillions of tiny atoms. So it's a start.

The Danish success of making an object move a half-metre may mean a future where teleportation becomes a reality. No more hanging around in French classes. No more waiting in one of those giant traffic jams in China. All you'll need is the latest smartphone app and a whisper of *"Beam me outta here!"*

## STRAIGHT TO FRANCE. DOH!

# DOOMSDAY MACHINE

**D**oomsday isn't what it used to be.

In days gone by, the end of the world was seen as myth and fantasy, like the idea of The Four Horsemen of the Apocalypse. The Four Horsemen (Conquest, War, Famine, and Death) appear in chapter six of the Book of Revelations in the Christian Bible. When these guys appear, the apocalypse won't be too far behind.

All that changed with the rise of modern science. Science fiction, a new type of fantasy, was now able to imagine a more believable way of destroying the world.

Mary Shelley's *The Last Man* (1826) featured a future industrial world stricken by a global plague. MP Shiel's timeless tale *The Purple Cloud* (1901) saw the calamitous leak of a chemical gas, killing all the people on the planet. Then, HG Wells invented the atom bomb. His 1914 novel *The World Set Free* 'inspired' egghead Leo Szilárd to actually build one.

The fictional doomsday device became fact. The threat of global nuclear war loomed and the Doomsday Clock became its symbol.

The symbol was founded in 1947 by the University of Chicago magazine *The Bulletin of the Atomic Scientists* and it has been used to represent the Doomsday Clock ever since.

The magazine uses the idea of the fate of the human race as being at a time that is 'minutes to midnight'. Midnight is doomsday. The end of time.

The clock currently reads 11:55. Thanks to science fiction.

# TIME AS THE FOURTH DIMENSION

**O**ur world has four dimensions. Three dimensions are space and the fourth is time. Seems obvious, doesn't it? And yet it took English fiction writer HG Wells to spell it out.

The time traveller (sounds like the Doctor!) in Wells' famous 1895 novel *The Time Machine* explains it like this:

*"There is no difference between Time and any of the three dimensions of Space, except that our consciousness moves along it."*

Now, this notion was nothing new: connecting time with space had a long history going all the way back to Greek boffin Aristotle, who was teacher to the famous conqueror Alexander the Great. Even though the beginning of the machine age in the 1800s had led to an obsession with time, most people thought of the fourth dimension as something to do with space. HG Wells wasn't buying it, so he opened up a new and exciting chapter in the history of ideas!

## TIME WAS ON THE TIP OF EVERYONE'S TONGUE.

Take modern art. Time was splashed upon the canvas of the

Cubists; a group of painters who were trying to paint in four dimensions. Artists like Pablo Picasso made paintings where various viewpoints were visible at the same time. All dimensions were used to give the painting a greater sense of depth. It was a revolutionary new way of looking at things!

Time was also captured in cinema, and in stop-motion photography, where a series of static photos are made to appear as if the subject in them moves on its own. Techniques like these inspired Italian painter Giacomo Balla to paint *Dynamism of a Dog on a Leash*. The dog has eight countable tails, and its legs are lost in a wash of blur. Four swinging dog leads can also be seen. But the painting gives a tremendous sense of movement in time.

Physics caught the time fever. Albert Einstein came up with

the theory of relativity in 1905. At first Einstein said there were three space dimensions, and time. But soon everyone started talking about time as the fourth dimension, thanks to HG Wells, and the notion of space-time was born!

Time was never the same again.

Einstein gave us a scientific perspective on the fourth dimension: Moving clocks run slow. Time is slowed down by gravity. And the speed of light is the same no matter how the observer is moving.

## IT WAS A REVOLUTION IN TIME!

All this seemed to worry Spanish painter Salvador Dali, whose pictures were rather odd to begin with. In response to Einstein, Dali produced one of his most famous paintings, *The Persistence of Memory*. The painting's floppy clocks are history's most graphic example of gravity distorting time.

The obsession with the fourth dimension continued.

One fascination was the time paradox. This can be nut-shelled by one question:

*"What would happen if I went back in time and killed my own grandad?"*

The skill of tampering with time in this way reached its genius peak with a story called *All You Zombies* (1959), by Robert A Heinlein. The main character of the story moves back and foward in time, manages to change gender, and becomes his/her own mother and father! WEIRD.

A second attraction was something called *The Butterfly Effect*. The idea was first floated in fiction by Ray Bradbury's story *A Sound of Thunder* (1952). A time-tourist wreaks havoc by treading on a pre-historic butterfly and unleashing an alternative world. The tale reminds the reader that small changes have huge consequences in time. And we know from these days of climate change how true THAT can be!

# TIME TRAVEL

**C**onsider this: Albert Einstein is flying through the Universe at the speed of light.

In front of Albert, and at arm's length, is a mirror. The mirror is *also* travelling at the speed of light. The question is: if Albert looks into the mirror, does he see his own reflection? Or has he become a vampire?! At the tender age of sixteen, and in the same year HG Wells wrote *The Time Machine*, this *gedanken,* or thought experiment, puzzled Einstein greatly (well, OK, not the vampire bit).

Since Albert would be effectively sitting on top of a light beam, light from him would never catch up with the mirror. His image would disappear. This all struck Einstein as rather odd. He did not believe it. His solution to this puzzle was revolutionary: he rewrote physics and the concept of time!

Before Einstein the maximum speed possible was thought to be infinite. But Albert proposed that everyone sees the same speed for light, no matter how they are moving. Not only that, but Albert showed that the speed of light was the maximum speed possible.

Albert then wondered what happens if you try to get a massive object (we might propose the TARDIS) to go beyond the speed of light. This light speed barrier is one of the results of special relativity theory, developed by Einstein in 1905.

To speed along, you need energy. To travel at the speed of light, the amount of energy needed to propel you swells to infinity! To move the TARDIS at the speed of light would take all the energy in the Universe. To get round this, the clever *Doctor Who* writer Robert Holmes invented the Eye of Harmony, where the Time Lords suspended time around an exploding star as it became a black hole, harnessing the potential energy that would never occur. Eh?! **GOBBLEDYGOOK?** Yes. But it doesn't always have to be. Writing science fiction is quite often a kind of thought experiment. Fiction writers invent different universes and then ask 'what if?' questions about what might happen in such a universe.

The faster-than-light speculation of science fiction began with French writer Camille Flammarion. Flammarion wrote a pre-Einstein fantasy, *Lumen* (1867), in which he predicts some of the effects of faster-than-light travel.

Flammarion dreamt up

spacetime. Thirty years before Einstein, *Lumen* was the first novel to propose that time and space were not absolute. They exist, said Flammarion, only relative to one another. He also explained how travelling faster than light would make history run in reverse!

Much of the science fiction of the early twentieth century chose to ignore Einstein's findings. Probably because the writers didn't understand them. Soon enough, though, such ignorance became unfashionable. In its place popped up a cottage industry of ideas and devices – ideas such as the 'space warp' into 'hyperspace', along with black hole and wormhole travel.

In the imagined world of *Star Trek*, for example, the warp drive is the preferred form of faster-than-light propulsion. So sophisticated is the warp drive that spacecraft like the USS Enterprise jauntily zoom to many multiples of the speed of light.

But hang on. In these days of video calls, why couldn't we just *phone* ET, rather than go all the way to Planet Zog to visit? Will faster-than-light communication be possible?

## WELL, SCIENCE FICTION HAS THOUGHT OF THAT TOO.

In a 2013 episode of *Doctor Who* entitled *Nightmare in Silver,* a character talks about a broken Ansible communicator. Now, an Ansible is a famous device invented in science fiction in 1966. It's a machine capable of communicating instantaneously across the gulfs of space!

So you can chat to bug-eyed monsters without having to get into your spaceship. The Ansible pops up a lot in science fiction, for example, if you listen carefully, you will spot one being mentioned in the 2013 movie *Ender's Game*.

# TIME MACHINES

OK, your time machine is built. Where first? To the empire of the Romans? To our bright future of sleek and nimble spaceships? Or to sail the seven seas with medieval pirates? Pirates? Good choice!

TEMPORAL CAMSHAFT. CHECK.
FOURTH-DIMENSIONAL PERAMBULATOR. CHECK.
IGNITION. CHECK.

Ignition?! Hang on a minute. Exactly how are these time machines meant to work?

One of the very first time gadgets was invented by Charles Lutwidge Dodgson, better known as Lewis Carroll, the fella who wrote about Alice in Wonderland. His time machine idea? The Outlandish Watch. Appearing in Carroll's story *Sylvie and Bruno* (1889), the watch had two modes. If the reverse peg was pushed, then "events of the next hour happen in reverse order". The other mode involved the watch's hands. They could be moved backwards, as much as a month, enabling the wearer of the watch to travel into the past.

Sadly, you won't find one of these little beauties at the local jewellers. I've already checked, and the jeweller looked at me as if I was mad! In the story the device's owner, a Professor, for heaven's sake, is frustratingly cagey when asked to describe the theoretical basis for the thingamajig:

*"I could explain it, but you would not understand it."*

He could at least *try*!

HG Wells fared no better. He cunningly left the details of his time machine extremely fuzzy. It was left to others to figure out. French writer Alfred Jarry stuck his neck out in a review of Wells' *Time Machine* called *A Commentary to Serve for the Practical Construction of the Machine to Explore Time.* PHEW!

Wells had talked vaguely of levers. But Jarry unduly designed his machine with three rotating gyrostats (rotating wheels pivoted within rigid cases). He even included an impressive nonsense diagram. Jarry figured that a time machine would have to anchor itself absolutely in space in order to move in time. In this way, he says, "all future and past instants… would be explored successively". YEAH, RIGHT.

Kurt Vonnegut's race of fictional aliens, the Tralfamadorians, had gone even further. With no contraption of any kind, they were naturally able to see along the timeline of the Universe. They not only had the ability to experience all four dimensions. They also had total recall of both past and future AT THE SAME TIME! The human view of time is a mere snapshot. The Tralfamadorian's is that of a movie in which all scenes are played out at once.

So, how feasible is HG Wells' fictional trip into the far future? Professor of Theoretical Physics Paul Davies addressed such questions in his 2001 book *How to Build a Time Machine.* If we want to travel into the future, all we need is a machine that can move at a velocity close to the speed of light. As our spaceship approaches this speed, the slower time moves. Once you get back to Earth, you will hardly have aged. Decades, or even centuries, will have passed 'back home'.

According to physicist, J Richard Gott, in his 2002 book *Time Travel in Einstein's Universe*, travelling back in time is far trickier. It entails fiddling with wormholes, cosmic strings, or black holes. These are the kind of time machines feasible only with mind-warping technology.

And in 2007 American scientist Ronald Mallett broke the news of his lifelong struggle to build a time machine. Mallett's take on time travel is to bend spacetime. Massive objects such as stars and planets can bend spacetime. Mallett is among those who believe that a machine can also be used to bend the continuum. So, rather than the De Lorean car envisaged in the *Back to the Future* films, Mallett's machine is a ring laser, an extremely powerful one. And maybe one day, by simply popping into this huge vortex of light, travel through time may be possible.

# Try This at Home

## BUILDING YOUR OWN TIME MACHINE

Unlike black holes, which are one-way journeys to oblivion, a wormhole has two mouths. An exit, and an entrance. Some scientists believe you can keep a wormhole's throat open by using a force opposed to gravity. Kind of antigravity, if you like.

SO, THE STUFF OF FICTION MAY ONE DAY BECOME FACT.

HERE'S A RECIPE FOR A WORMHOLE:

- Take a dash of exotic matter
- Make sure this matter is made up of particles that have antigravity properties
- Pop them into the throat of a wormhole
- Bingo! The wormhole throat stops imploding, and...

...YOU'VE MADE A TIME MACHINE!

# PRE-CRIME

Imagine being able to predict events in time before they actually happen.

That's what happens in the 2002 movie *Minority Report*, which is based on a 1956 story by famous science fiction writer Philip K Dick. In the story people with this ability are used in a 'PreCrime' division of the Washington DC police force. They see crime before it occurs and, with the aid of cops and computers, stop that crime from taking place.

In the movie Tom Cruise plays a cool cop who hurries from place to place, eagerly trying to stop 'pre-criminals'. Then he finds he has been framed, and that the PreCrime system has been turned into a kind of Big Brother state in which you are condemned for what you are going to do, even before you've done it!

The TV series *Person of Interest* is based on a similar premise: a former CIA officer is recruited by a mysterious billionaire egghead to prevent predicted crimes from taking place.

Now, pre-crime is in danger of flipping over from fiction into fact. The New York Police Technical Department is working on its own 'pre-crime' system. It uses computers to predict when and where crimes will occur. NYPD's first success was when it successfully predicted a street robbery on 27th July 2005, between the hours of 8pm and midnight on South Broadway, New York. As forecast, a woman was robbed of her mobile phone at 8:44pm. Officers were already at hand, and they were able to arrest the armed suspects immediately.

So if this kind of thing carries on in the future, be careful about not only what you do, but also what you *plan* to do!

"YOU'RE NICKED - FOR NEXT WEEK'S ROBBERY!"

# WORMHOLES

You're standing at the Crucifixion.

Dumbstruck and open-mouthed, you can't help but stare at the scene. Perhaps the most famous in all of history. It was an expensive package. But your Time Travel Tour operator said it would be well worth your parents' cash. Just one thing to remember: You must do nothing to disrupt history.

## NOTE TO SELF:
## DON'T TREAD ON ANY
## BUTTERFLIES THIS TIME!

And when the crowd is asked who should be saved, you join in with the call, *"Give us Barabbas!"*

Suddenly, you realise something strange about the crowd. Not a single soul from 33 AD is present. The mob condemning Jesus to the cross is made up 'lock, stock and smoking barrel' of tourists from the future.

Isn't this a great time travel story? It's called 'Let's Go to Golgotha', and it was written by a guy called Garry Kilworth in 1975. Like many other writers, Garry was enchanted by the idea of time travel. After all, if you could go *anywhere* in space and time, just where would you go first? Ancient Rome? Or Greece, perhaps? The days of the Great Fire of London, maybe? Or the bloody times of The French Revolution?

But perhaps the best bit of the story is that this entire scene is not only littered with other tourists from the future; they actually CHANGE the outcome of history itself by being present at the Crucifixion. The time tourists think they know the way the story is meant to go. Rather than Jesus being set free, the crowd are meant to choose Barabbas, the bandit. But the decision only goes that way because the time tourists are witness to the scene. Would Jesus have been set free instead if they hadn't interfered? AAAARRGGH! It's enough to do your head in. Otherwise known as a paradox.

This kind of whacky paradox, which is often thrown up in time travel, is one of the reasons Professor Stephen Hawking refused to believe such travel was possible. His argument goes something like this: 'if time travel really IS possible, then where are the time tourists of the future? Why aren't they visiting us, telling us all about the joys of time travel?' He's obviously never met the Doctor.

Of course, the lack of time tourists today doesn't mean time travel isn't possible. It might just mean they find these times of ours too dull for a visit! Or it might mean that in some possible future timelines, time travel hasn't been developed. YET!

And even if time travel IS developed, there may be snags.

Assume we create a wormhole. A wormhole is a region of space that's warped. It's basically a 'shortcut' in space and time through which to travel. Trouble is, though, time travellers would not be able to travel back in time to a date before the wormhole was created.

So, for example, if scientists managed to build a wormhole on January 1st, 2050, they wouldn't be able to go back in time BEFORE 2050. This might explain why we've not been overrun by tourists.

### WE'VE SIMPLY NOT CREATED A WORMHOLE YET.

Famous science fiction writer John Campbell was the man who invented 'space warps'. In his 1931 story *Islands of Space* John used the idea as a shortcut from one region of space to another. And in his 1934 story *The Mightiest Machine*, he called this same shortcut 'hyperspace', another now-familiar phrase.

A year later, world famous Nobel Prize winning scientist Albert Einstein, with his colleague Nathan Rosen, came up with the science fact behind the science fiction invention of time travel. They worked out the scientific theory that explained the notion of 'bridges' in space. It was much later that scientists started calling these bridges 'wormholes'.

## WHAT DOES A WORMHOLE LOOK LIKE?

A wormhole has at least two mouths, connected to a single throat. And scientists really DO believe they exist, at least in theory. Einstein's worked it out – and no one is disagreeing at the moment. Stuff may 'travel' from one mouth to the other by passing through the wormhole. We haven't found one yet, but the Universe is immense. And we haven't really been looking very long. You've probably seen one on *Doctor Who*. They're the kind of swirly cosmic tunnel that you often see the TARDIS disappearing down.

The appearance of wormholes in our imaginations owes almost everything to fiction. 'The Rift' which also appears in *Doctor Who* is a wormhole.

In the 2008 film *Space Chimps*, some chimps go to rescue a $5 billion NASA probe that disappears into a wormhole. And in the cartoon *Invader Zim*, wormholes lead to other universes, such as a universe of pure itchiness!

# ALTERNATIVE HISTORIES

**W**hat if Hitler had won World War II? What if Guy Fawkes had blown up Parliament in 1605? What if you hadn't picked up this book and started to read these words? What if you'd decided to grab a sandwich instead? Perhaps there's a universe in which these 'what if?' things happened.

Big or small, these 'what if?' events are potentially the triggers to set off other timelines, generally known as alternative histories. Boffins use fictional 'what ifs?' as 'thought experiments' to help understand real history. When *Doctor Who* first hit our screens, a science teacher and history teacher hung around with the Doctor, and the audience was taken on a fantastic journey of 'what ifs?' in the time and space machine TARDIS. Using 'the' as a prefix came later.

## SO, WHERE DID IT ALL START?

An early 'what if?' book was about the French leader Napoleon. The book was written in 1836 by Geoffroy-Chateau and was called *Napoleon and the Conquest of the World*. PRETTY AMBITIOUS, OUI?!

Napoleon and Hitler, even though they lived over a

hundred years apart, are both thought to have made a big mistake in attacking Russia. IT'S BIG! IT'S FULL OF RUSSIANS! AND IT'S FREEZING! The military careers of the two leaders didn't go so well, after risking it with the Ruskies. And the Napoleon 'what if?' book suggests an alternative history, in which the French leader isn't defeated in his Russian campaign of 1812, but goes on to be victorious throughout Europe. IN HIS DREAMS!

HG Wells became one of the first writers to mash up 'what ifs?' with time travel.

In *The Time Machine*, the time traveller becomes the cause of the 'what if?' and it's because of his actions, that a divergence in time happens. Another similar HG Wells story is *Men Like Gods,* written in 1923. In this tale, travellers are transported to an alternate Earth created by a 'what if?' event. The planet is now a utopia, which means a kind of perfect world.

WHAT IF WE WERE DESCENDED FROM REPTILES INSTEAD OF APES?

In 1931 a huddle of historians (OK, it might not be a huddle, dear reader, but I'm guessing at what we might call a 'bunch' of historians) shared their thoughts about vital events in history and how they may have gone differently.

Then, in 1964, a Nobel-prize winning boffin, Robert William Fogel, used a 'what if?' approach to show how important railroads had been to the history of the United States. He painted a picture of an alternative US, one that had relied only on wagons, canals, and rivers, rather than the railroads. He was able to show that the US would have been much the same.

Today, alternative histories are everywhere. *Doctor Who*, in its continuing use of this theme, follows a long line of other series which use 'what ifs', like *The Time Tunnel* (1966), *The Tomorrow People* (1973), *Quantum Leap* (1989), *Sliders* (1995), *Heroes* (2006) and *Fringe* (2008).

And the video games genre has masses of 'what ifs?' to choose from. Games which follow the 'Nazis win World War II' theme, such as *Wolfenstein: The New Order* through to the wonderful *Assassin's Creed* series.

# IMMORTALITY

s the Doctor immortal?

Time was when Time Lords such as the Doctor could regenerate only twelve times before they shuffled off their alien but mortal coil. The secret first slipped out back in a 1976 episode, *The Deadly Assassin*, when it was first revealed that the 13th Doctor would be the last.

But in *The Death of the Doctor*, a 2010 episode of *The Sarah Jane Adventures*, the Doctor is asked how many times he can regenerate. He says there is no limit. We later find out that John Hurt is the War Doctor (the real 9th), and David Tennant wastes one his regenerations, making Capaldi arguably the 14th Doctor. CURIOUS.

The search for immortality has been a persistent human obsession. Although immortal creatures can be found in myths and fairytales, modern science might actually provide the means of achieving immortality. So it's been science fiction that has kept that immortal spark in the imagination over the last couple of centuries.

Immortality's founding mistress in sci-fi is Mary Shelley. Her 1833 book *The Mortal Immortal* features a hero who doesn't use magic to extend his life, as they may have done in the old myths, but instead uses science. Sadly, his fate is to watch his companions wither and die as he continues alone. He becomes a kind of traveller in time, always fated to move forward.

## IT'S ALMOST AS IF MARY SHELLEY INVENTED THE DOCTOR!

But what science does sci-fi use to keep the spark of life alive? The menu is a varied one, running from treatments and medicines, such as eugenics and genetic engineering, all the way through to artificially extending life, with the use of synthetic organs or becoming a cyborg. Another option for immortality in sci-fi revolves around the Internet. The idea being that, with further advances in computer technology in the future, we would be able to upload our personalities to live forever on the web. This idea goes all the way back to 1930, when British writer Olaf Stapledon wrote *Last and First Men*. In the book organic human-like brains are grown into machines. The idea is taken even further in the 1967 story *Lord of Light*, by Roger Zelazny. In this tale the crew of a space vessel become immortal by uploading their consciousness into new bodies. They do this so many times that they begin to see themselves as gods!

Boffins call this new kind of consciousness 'ARTIFICIAL INTELLIGENCE', of course. They realize that we don't currently have the technology to be able to do this kind of consciousness transfer yet, but with the fast pace of change in technology, it could well be on the horizon.

# TOP 10
## TIME MACHINES

## 1    The TARDIS

Time machine belonging to the Doctor. The TARDIS (Time And Relative Dimension In Space) is famously bigger on the inside, which is a cool design feature. Another design feature, the Chameleon Circuit, which allowed the TARDIS to blend with its immediate surroundings, broke early on, fixing it as a phone box. It's said to have travelled over 100 trillion years, from before the Big Bang to the edge of time itself.

## 2    DeLorean DMC-12

Spacetime auto belonging to crazy-haired inventor Dr Emmett Brown, from *Back to the Future*. The whole design focused on the car's Flux Capacitor. And in the words of the Doc: *"if you're gonna build a time machine into a car, why not do it with some style?"* Why not, indeed. It apparently needs 2.21 GigaWatts of energy at 88mph to work.

## 3    The Time Machine

Little is said of the Time Machine in HG Wells' original 1895 book. So when they made the movie in 1960, they let their imaginations run wild. This is, of course, the original and, many still believe, the best and most elegant contraption: all brass, glass, and dials. With its red leather padded seat, it's exactly the kind of beast you imagine a Victorian time-travelling gent would 'drive'.

# 4 Phone Booth

Be honest, surely this one is based on the TARDIS? The Phone Booth is from the comic time-travelling 1988 movie *Bill and Ted's Excellent Adventure*. It doesn't seem to have the quirkiness of the TARDIS, and totally lacks the bigger-on-the-inside thing, but does its job with more precision. *"Gentlemen, we're history."*

# 5 Outlandish Watch

The early-doors time gadget from the 1889 Lewis Carroll story, *Sylvie and Bruno*. True, the watch was limited to only two modes, one of which enabled the wearer to travel a month into the past. But otherwise you have to say it's a useful clothing accessory.

# 6 Projector-Collector

The 1995 movie *Twelve Monkeys* featured this projector-collector contraption, which enabled Bruce Willis to be pinged back in time to trace the outbreak of a deadly virus. Trouble was, it seemed the machine wouldn't work unless the time traveller was naked, which *could* get awkward.

# 7 Looper Time Machine

The time machine from the 2012 movie *Looper* looks a lot like a space capsule with a bunch of spaghetti wiring and two huge batteries fixed to the door. They can't possibly power the thing, surely? Looks cool but who would seriously travel back in time just to kill themselves, as the Loopers do?!

(https://www.youtube.com/watch?v=23JU5Cc_63A)

# 8 Childhood Diaries

Ever had that feeling of being transported back in time when reading a book or looking at a work of art? That's exactly what happens 'for real' in the 2004 movie *The Butterfly Effect*, only it's an old diary that provides the goods. Guy reads his own words and is transported back to the time when the words were written. Are written. Oh, you get the drift...

# 9 Time Displacement Sphere

The machine used for time travel in the trilogy of *Terminator* movies. OK, you may never actually *see* the device, and again folk appear to turn up naked after travel, but we get enough hints to know it's pretty slick. Trouble is, this machine seems to send you one way only. **STRANDED!**

# 10 Accelerating Chamber

The time machine in the alternative history TV series *Quantum Leap* seemed simple enough; just a puff of smoke in a darkened but futuristic looking room. On the negative side you only travel within your own lifetime and *could* end up in other people's bodies. EW, AND ALSO, EUGH.

# TOP 10
## SCI-FI MOVIES

## 1  2001: A Space Odyssey (1968)

Film Facts: the last space travel movie before men landed on the Moon. 2001 has everything: human evolution, technology, artificial intelligence, and extraterrestrial life. The space sequences of the film were so real that NASA used them for training.

THINGS THEY SAID: *"to enjoy '2001' you must tune your brain to a different wavelength"* and *"...reaches for the stars and finds itself, against all odds, on the other side of them."*

## 2  Metropolis (1927)

Film Facts: the most expensive movie ever made at the time (in modern money around $200million), Metropolis is set in a future society so drab that the wealthy son of the city's ruler wants to lead a revolution. Among other things, the film boasted a cast of 30,000 extras.

THINGS THEY SAID: *"the first true masterpiece of science fiction in film."*

## 3   Blade Runner (1982)

Film Facts: November 2019, dystopian Los Angeles, and a batch of genetically engineered replicants are on the run, hunted down by special police known as 'Blade Runners'. A nightmare world dominated by mega-corporations. Sound familiar? Based on the book *Do Androids Dream of Electric Sheep?*

THINGS THEY SAID: *"A glorious, timeless nightmare."*

## 4   Alien (1979)

Film Facts: a bold blend of sci-fi and horror, Alien is about a highly aggressive extraterrestrial creature that stalks and kills the crew of a spaceship. The story's sole survivor, Ripley, is one of cinema's great female heroes.

THINGS THEY SAID: *"The dark, cold beauty of this film will never be equalled."*

## 5   Solaris (1972)

Film Facts: a space station in orbit around another world finds life below, but the alien is an ocean that engulfs the entire planet. Scientists journey to the world of Solaris to try understand it. The movie's moral? The stars are not for man.

THINGS THEY SAID: *"Solaris will haunt you for years to come."*

## 6 ET: The Extra-Terrestrial (1982)

Film Facts: mostly filmed from an adult-waist-height perspective, ET is about a lonely boy who befriends an extraterrestrial that is stuck on Earth. With his family and friends, he helps the alien return home, while keeping ET secret from the government and The Man. Nominated for nine Oscars, winning four.

THINGS THEY SAID: *"I would happily give Steven Spielberg a hug for his timeless gift to the world."*

## 7 Star Wars (1977)

Film Facts: a long time ago in a galaxy far, far away, a group of freedom fighters plot to destroy the evil Empire's powerful Death Star space station. An adventure story which replaces six-shooters with light swords, and horses with spaceships.

THINGS THEY SAID: "Star Wars *made epic fantasy real."*

## 8 Close Encounters of the Third Kind (1977)

Film Facts: the tale of an ordinary guy whose life changes after an encounter with a UFO. The movie's special effects bonanza represents alien contact as a gateway to new knowledge and a higher consciousness.

THINGS THEY SAID: *"Build a monolith, and they will come."*

# 9 The Terminator (1984)

Film Facts: a time-travel thriller in which an android assassin is sent back from 2029 to kill the woman who gives birth to the man who saves the world. Man versus machine, grey matter versus computer, past versus present versus future. State-of-the-art at the time, and still packs a knockout punch.

THINGS THEY SAID: *"A brilliant sci-fi film that cleverly combines strong storytelling with suspense and killer set-pieces..."*

# 10 The Matrix (1999)

Film Facts: erm, tricky. A bleak future in which the reality as seen by most humans is actually fake; it is in fact a simulation called The Matrix, created by machines to keep humans trapped while using their bodies heat and electricity to power their machine world. PHEW. There's also fighting, bleeding-edge special effects, killer robots, evil authority geezers, conspiracy theories, and, best of all, Neo – a social outcast who becomes a flying kung-fu Jesus. "Get me an exit!"

THINGS THEY SAID: "The Matrix *is a new kind of movie, a visionary mixture of technology, philosophy and thrilling action!"*

# TOP 10 GAMES

*What are the best electronic games that have science fiction in their gameplay?*

## 1  Half-Life 2 (2004)

Gameworld: an alternate history of our planet, where the resources of Earth, including humans, are being harvested by an empire known as the Combine. Includes blistering action, heart-stopping set-pieces, ground-breaking physics, and leading-edge AI. Like a mega-budget disaster movie written by George Orwell.

**THINGS THEY SAID:** *"Half-Life 2 is the game of the decade."*

## 2  Mass Effect 2 (2010)

Gameworld: set in the Milky Way in the 22nd century, where inter-star travel is possible and a machine race of starships known as the Reapers are said to wipe out all organic civilisations every 50,000 years. **GULP!**

**THINGS THEY SAID:** *"Mass Effect 2 is bloody brilliant. Grab a fork, and tuck in."*

## 3  XCOM Enemy Unknown (2012)

Gameworld: set in the near future, where an alien invasion begins. Earth sets up XCOM (EXtraterrestrial Combat Unit), the most elite army of soldiers and boffins ever organized, to defend us from the alien attack. Set your combat rifle to 'kill'!

THINGS THEY SAID: *"XCOM is an experience that gets under your skin."*


## 4  Fallout 3 (2008)

Gameworld: it's the year 2277, 200 years after a nuclear holocaust. The setting is the Wasteland, and retro-future. You are let out of Vault 101 as the game begins. Radscorpions, molerats, and mirelurks lie in wait...

THINGS THEY SAID: *"A scary vision of the future, but it's impossible to not be swept away by it."*


## 5  Starcraft 2 (2010)

Gameworld: mission–based game which revolves around the rivalry between three species: humans, the Zerg, and the Protoss. At the time of its release, it became the fastest selling strategy game of all time.

THINGS THEY SAID: *"The light bulb, penicillin, mathematics, democracy... They're all important inventions... But none of them were ever as much fun as StarCraft."*

## 6 Star Wars: Knights of the Old Republic (2003)

Gameworld: 4000 years before the rise of the Galactic Empire, in the Golden Age of the Republic, when Jedi and Sith number in the thousands, your actions decide the outcome of a colossal war. EPIC!

THINGS THEY SAID: *"One of the 100 greatest video games of all time."*

## 7 Portal 2 (2011)

Gameworld: the events in Portal 2 take place in the Half-Life game universe. As a subject you have to navigate yourself out of some dangerous 'test chambers', in the company of an AI named GLaDOS who seems to have killed the previous inmates. UH OH!

THINGS THEY SAID: *"Funny, clever, mentally stimulating and always good honest fun."*

## 8 Halo 4 (2012)

Gameworld: it's the year 2557 and space-faring humanity are battling the Covenant, an alien collection of species menacing the Galaxy. The Halo ringworlds in this series have a long history in science fiction books.

THINGS THEY SAID: *"Halo 4 continues the Halo series' reign as one of the premier shooter franchises."*

## 9 Saints Row 4 (2013)

Gameworld: an alien race, the Zin, have destroyed Earth and murdered seven billion people. As one of Earth's last survivors, you combat the invasion by completing madcap missions. Oh, and you're President of the United States. You can't say it's not bold.

THINGS THEY SAID: *"The silliest game in the world with absolutely everything in it, including an alien invasion."*

## 10 Doctor Who: The Gunpowder Plot (2011)

Gameworld: it's 1605 and an intricate gaming web begins, involving the Doctor, Amy, Rory, the Rutans and Sontarans, the TARDIS and Guy Fawkes' Gunpowder Plot. Yep, you read that right.

THINGS THEY SAID: *Boom!*

The robots are coming.

The 21st century will see the rise of a robot army that will revolutionise life on our planet just as much as the Internet did in the last couple of decades.

That's the prediction. And you can see why many people believe it. The stuff of fiction is fast becoming fact. The US army is making BigDog, a four-legged mechanical pack-carrying robot. Guided by its own sensors, BigDog can travel through dangerous terrain while carrying 150kg on its back. And in the air robot drones are busy gliding over the globe, stalking targets or keeping peace.

We all love machines and we each have a favourite. Maybe it's a games console or perhaps a smartphone. Maybe you've got a soft spot for that 50" flatscreen TV.

## WHAT WOULD WE DO WITHOUT THEM?!

But many writers of science fiction have warned for some time that we may be sleepwalking into the Droid Age, and that too few people are debating the consequences.

Are sci-fi writers making too much of our attachment to machines? Are machines really going to take over? Maybe not just yet, but the way in which we rely on them is beyond doubt.

On Twitter a quarter of all tweets are actually created by 'bots', computer programs that do automatic tasks. Half of the Internet traffic clicking through our websites is not human. On Wikipedia twenty-two of the thirty busiest Wikipedia editors are bots.

And machines seem to be after our money. 70% of trade on the Wall Street stock market is automatic – in the UK it is 30% – so when money markets get busy, we rely even more on bots and algorithms.

The robot has always been one of science fiction's most famous machines. A legion of Terminators, Droids, Replicants and AIs litter the history of sci-fi. And they are rarely good guys. They often seem keen to disembowel us and wear our entrails as a hat. Mad doctors in sci-fi are forever creating machines that turn on their creator. It's as if they are trying to spell it out for us loud and clear: the creation of machines will not end well!

Yet, this was not always the case. Sci-fi writers have also dreamt of futures in which machines are our friends, of sparkling cities with metal spires in which labour-saving droids work hard to serve our every need. It seems we have become mistrustful of machines. Maybe as we have come to depend on them more, we have become aware of how wrong things could go if there was a revolt of the robots.

In this Machine section you'll find examples of some of the ideas, technologies and machines that have crossed from fact to fiction, and from fiction to fact.

These days, to say that a certain boffin or writer is the 'inventor' of a technology is to ignore the armies of other boffins and writers who have helped make a reality out of the initial spark of an idea. Mixed in with 'big' ideas such as the Internet, robots, and machine intelligence you will also find more curious entries like liquid metal, Big Brother, and the mobile phone.

All these ideas and more have helped create the futureworld that we live in today. From the way we are able to communicate instantly with the world, to the ability we have to live our lives without ever having to talk to anyone at all.

Science and science fiction have been busy inventing the future, and as you will see, the machine has played an important role.

# CYBERSPACE

In June 2013 the United States declared war on China! Not that anyone would have noticed very much. The war wasn't carried out on land, at sea, or in the air. It was instead carried out in cyberspace. This kind of electronic warfare, known as a cyberattack, has become a daily event in the modern age. And it's not just the US making the attacks; China does too. And so do a number of countries that have the technology and boffins to do it. Cyberspace has become dangerous.

## BUT WHAT IS THIS MYSTERIOUS CYBERSPACE?

The word cyberspace was first used by sci-fi writer William Gibson, in his 1982 short story 'Burning Chrome'. Gibson described cyberspace as a combination of the words *cybernetics* and *space*. Cyberspace has grown to dominate our modern world, not just for work, rest and play, but also to wage war.

In 'Burning Chrome' a futuristic world has become dominated by electronics, just like our own world. In his 1984 story *Neuromancer* William Gibson sends his hero on a journey into cyberspace. But all is not what it seems. When the hero gets there, it seems to exist nowhere and yet everywhere.

Another sci-fi writer, Bruce Sterling, described cyberspace as the place where your telephone conversation *appears* to happen. It's an empty space, set up by the people who are making the telephone call. It seems completely real to the callers, yet it doesn't exist.

The same kind of thing happens when you use the Internet. When you log on and browse the World Wide Web, you are entering a realm that both does and does not exist. Although you are physically connected to the network of computers, you actually enter some kind of alternate reality. AAAAARRRRGGGGHHHH! WEIRD.

In the 1982 film *Tron* the world's greatest video game creator, Kevin Flynn, is digitized into a virtual reality grid. In the 2010 sequel *Tron: Legacy* his son, Sam Flynn, follows

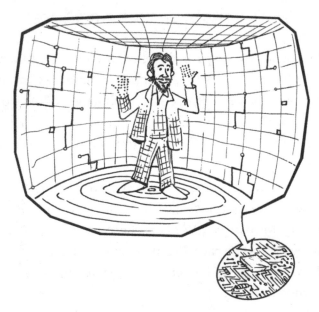

him there to experience virtual reality gladiators and the alternate reality of cyberspace. Not only that, they are represented in this brave new world of cyberspace as avatars.

Our own 'personal' avatars wander through cyberspace in a comparable alternate reality. This is known as cyberculture, and it's a real alternative to our own existence. **YET IT'S NOT ALL PLAY!** Already several people have used cyberspace as a chance to do business and have become real life millionaires.

Websites and social media, like Twitter and Facebook, all exist in cyberspace. And your very own Facebook page exists in a kind of electronic limbo, waiting to be viewed by a visitor in cyberspace.

So, if you haven't yet dived into this alternative reality invented by sci-fi and made real by computer eggheads, it's about time you took a virtual ride into cyberspace!

# MACHINE INTELLIGENCE

**W**ill machines ever be able to think? Will there ever be such a thing as machine intelligence?

Perhaps your iPod is sulking as we speak. Or maybe your mobile is moping as you haven't sent a text in over three minutes. As far as we know, machines are not able to think as humans do, although in many ways we are also machines. Biological machines.

Of course, machine intelligence was a topic explored in science fiction long before science got around to it.

Robots started the ball rolling. It all began when French boffin Blaise Pascal (isn't that a great name?!) invented a basic calculator in 1642, and a German egghead, Gottfried Liebniz refined it in 1671 by including multiplication and division to the calculator's functions. But it was the British inventor Charles Babbage who made the biggest change. In the 1820s he laid the basis for science fiction stories with his pioneering work on computing machines that could be programmed.

Not long after Charles Darwin and Alfred Russel Wallace came up with the idea of evolution, science fiction writer Samuel Butler wondered if the evolution idea might apply to machines. In his 1872 book *Erewhon* (an anagram of 'nowhere'), Butler's hero travels to a fictional lost world. Once there, he finds a society that has banned all but the most basic technology. Why? Because they feared that machines would evolve, become more intelligent than their human masters and turn them into slaves. **GULP.**

Science fiction stories then began to flesh out the idea of these thinking machines, such as in the tales *The Thought Machine* by Ammianus Marcellinu, 1927, and *The Machine* by John W Campbell, 1935.

Real life thinking machines started to appear with the post-war creation of *ENIAC* (*Electronic Numerical Integrator And Computer*) in 1946. *ENIAC* was a big computer and it had many jobs, mostly to do with the US army. So already the first real thinking machine was associated with violence. **NOT GOOD.**

Then came HAL – the most famous killer computer in science fiction history.

He was an intelligent machine, an onboard space computer who decided he wanted humans doing things *his* way. HAL appears in perhaps one of the most famous science fiction films of all time, *2001: A Space Odyssey*, directed by Stanley Kubrick and released in 1968.

In a chilling sequence in the middle of the *2001* movie, this machine intelligence HAL 9000, having gone insane because of a programming error, tries to kill all the astronauts onboard the spaceship *Discovery*. What makes HAL even scarier, apart from his neutral, calculating voice, is his lack of body. He has no physical presence, and yet he can control his machine environment so that it is fatal to the crew.

Similarly, SkyNet, the machine intelligence in the 1984 sci-fi classic *Terminator*, has to find ways to 'reach out and touch' the soft squishy humans it wants to annihilate. SkyNet does this by using a wide variety of other machines under its control.

In reality, computer science is still some way behind the fiction. Although the academic field of machine intelligence was set up way back in 1956, artificial intelligence has so far not reached the levels then thought to be only decades away. In the meantime, keep an eye on your computer.

## BE VERY WARY OF YOUR VACUUM AND DON'T SIT FOR TOO LONG ON YOUR TOILET...

# HEAT RAY WEAPON

**E**ver got into a hot bath that's just too uncomfortable to sit in? Your brain tells you to get out of there at once. Brains are helpful like that.

When HG Wells was creating merciless Martians for his 1898 book *The War of the Worlds*, he chose heat as their main weapon. Wells wanted to give the reader the impression of the Martians being much more advanced than we mere Earthlings.

The Martian Tripods – an unstoppable force from outer space – tower over man. These superior machines are tools of human domination – as the Martians plan is to take over the Earth and start farming humans! What better way to conquer the planet than an *"invisible, inevitable sword of heat"* as Wells called it.

In early 2007 news broke that the US army had developed a revolutionary heat-ray weapon to drive back enemies and break up hostile crowds.

The weapon is actually called the Active Denial System. It beams out an invisible high-energy ray that induces a sudden burning feeling in its target audience. One nutty journalist who agreed to be blasted with the heat-ray said the feeling was like a blast from a very hot oven – too painful to put up with without diving for cover.

The US army says that, unlike the HG Wells heat-ray, their gun is harmless. It's just a way of making enemies surrender their weapons, bridging the gap between 'shouting and shooting'. One of the weapons of the future, it is expected to be on the market very soon.

# ATOM BOMB

*"...and these atomic bombs which science burst upon the world that night were strange, even to the men who used them."*

**T**hat's a quote from HG Wells' 1914 novel *The World Set Free*. Wells was not only the first to christen the 'atomic bomb' – he invented it. And his story led non-stop to Hiroshima.

By the dawn of the twentieth century, it was clear that some form of atomic energy was powering the stars. Scientists, such as the great nuclear physicist Ernest Rutherford, realised that atoms were capable of enormous energies. And even though Rutherford said, "*some fool in a laboratory might blow up the universe unawares*", he trusted nature to 'guard her secret'. HG Wells begged to differ.

His future vision of the making and use of the bomb is incredibly far-sighted. In *The World Set Free* the 1950s scientist who uncovers atomic energy realises that there is no going back. Nonetheless, he feels, *"like an imbecile who has presented a box of loaded revolvers to a crèche."* HG Wells envisaged a world war in 1956, with an alliance of France, England and America fighting against Germany and Austria.

The book predicts a holocaust. The world's major cities are annihilated by small atomic bombs dropped by aeroplanes. This is no mere guesswork. Wells' weapons are truly atomic – Einstein's idea of converting a small amount of matter into huge explosive energy, triggered by a chain reaction.

HG Wells' book influenced the brilliant Hungarian physicist Leo Szilárd to actually *make* the bomb. After reading *The World Set Free* in 1932, Szilárd became the first scientist to seriously examine the physics behind the fiction.

Szilárd was furious. He'd read an article in *The Times* newspaper by Rutherford, rejecting the idea of using atomic energy for practical purposes. His fury, along with his legendary intelligence, enabled Szilárd to dream up the very idea of the nuclear chain reaction needed for the bomb to work, while he waited for traffic lights to change on Southampton Row in Bloomsbury, London. One year later Szilárd filed for a patent on the idea of the bomb.

Leo Szilárd became the driving force behind the mission to build the bomb, known as the Manhattan Project. And it was Szilárd's idea to send a letter in August 1939 to US President Franklin D Roosevelt about the possibility of atomic weapons. As Jewish scientists, Szilárd and Einstein feared the irresistible rise of a Nazi Bomb.

Within months the Manhattan Project was launched. It would eventually employ around 130,000 people, at a total cost of $2 billion ($20 billion in today's figures). The project output? The explosion of three atomic weapons in 1945: the Trinity test detonation in July in New Mexico; a uranium bomb, 'Little Boy', detonated on August 6 over Hiroshima; and a plutonium bomb, 'Fat Man', discharged on August 9 over Nagasaki.

## WELLS' FICTION BECAME FACTUAL TERROR OVER JAPAN.

As the 320,000 inhabitants of Hiroshima were waking up, the bomb burst over the city. Thousands were slain in a second. Vapourised by light and energy... heat death. Their only remains, ghostly shadows on nearby walls. They were the lucky ones. Victims further from the blast were blinded or had their skin and hair set ablaze. Later they would lose the white blood cells needed to fight the escalating radiation poisoning.

Szilárd had hoped that President Truman would merely 'demonstrate' the bomb. Not use it against cities as in Wells' *The World Set Free*. But as the war raged on, scientists lost the power over their research.

The Manhattan Project's lead scientist, Robert Oppenheimer, mulled over the 'atomic bomb', first realised by Wells. Oppenheimer spoke for many scientists when he said:

*"In some sort of crude sense which no vulgarity, no humour, no overstatement can quite extinguish, the physicists have known sin: and this is a knowledge which they cannot lose."*

# MOBILE PHONES

**Y**ou need to call a friend. So you reach into your pocket, pull out the familiar rectangle shape. Swiping the screen, you dial up and hear your friend's voice reply from some distant shore. A common occurrence in today's interconnected world, sure. But in 1638?

## THAT'S THE YEAR SCIENCE FICTION INVENTED THE MOBILE PHONE.

The invention dawned in the most unlikely of places: a sci-fi story called *The Man in the Moone*, written by Francis Godwin, better known as the Bishop of Llandaff, in Cardiff, Wales. The story's hero uses a number of methods to communicate, including wireless sound messages. It's not difficult to see how the devices in this story are forerunners of today's mobile communicators.

In fact it would take another three centuries before mobile communicators became a reality. They developed from two-way radios and ship-to-shore telephones. It was only on 3 April 1973 that Motorola boffin Dr Martin Cooper decided to make a call to his rival Joel Engel (the head of research at AT&T's Bell Labs) while strolling through the city streets of New York.

## THE AGE OF THE MOBILE PHONE HAD TRULY BEGUN.

The concept design for Martin Cooper's phone was itself inspired by science fiction. In this case it was the famous communicators from the hit TV series *Star Trek*. So from the very beginnings, with Bishop Godwin through to making the idea a reality, it's been sci-fi that has enabled us all

to **BOLDLY CALL WHERE NO ONE HAS CALLED BEFORE.**

# THE INTERNET

**N**obody owns the Internet.

Okay, maybe you can purchase your own little bit of it. But no-one owns the whole thing. Think about it: the Internet is an entity, a global collection of networks, large and small, that put together is just too immense for any group or individual to own. Each and every time you log on, you are happily skipping your way along various networks connected together in many different ways. And it's from this idea of '*inter*connected *net*works' that we get the name Internet.

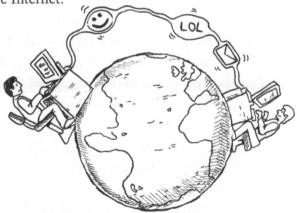

But long before you surfed along the information superhighway, science fiction writers were exploring the idea behind what we today recognise as the Internet. Back in 1937, good old HG Wells published a work called *The World Brain*. His idea was that knowledge on planet Earth was ever expanding and evolving.

*"There is no practical obstacle whatever now to the creation of an efficient index to all human knowledge, ideas and achievements, to the creation, that is, of a complete planetary memory for all mankind. And not simply an index; the direct reproduction of the thing itself can be summoned to any properly prepared spot,"* old Wellsy said.

**SOUND FAMILIAR?** Wells even seems to imply a wi-fi hot-spot in his prediction! When he wrote it, he was actually thinking about using microfilm, the stuff on which they sometimes hide secrets in old spy films. HG Wells was developing ideas that had been pioneered by Paul Otlet. He was a Belgian boffin and one of the founders of information science; the field of knowledge of how best to deal with data.

## THEN IN 1947 CAME THE FIRST SCIENCE FICTION STORY ABOUT THE INTERNET.

Murray Leinster's story *A Logic Named Joe* was about a group of workers sitting in front of 'logics'. These logics were large TV screens with keyboards attached. Using an invention called a 'carson circuit', the logics were able to punch up different sites across the logic network via different sets of 'tanks', which acted as server computers do in our own Internet today.

The logics were very versatile. From the latest weather forecast or international news to what's going on in the world of sport, all was available through a logic. The system even allowed you to type in the address of someone else's logic, so you could communicate with them in the same way as we do through email and messaging systems today. The carson circuit in each logic was its unique address, which meant that as well as being a physical thing, it also acted in the same way that a URL (Uniform Resource Locator) or web address does today.

It was not until 1962 that anything like Murray Leinster's sci-fi story became fact. In that year, the US Government's ARPA (Advanced Research Projects Agency; snappy title, eh?!) decided to link together three network terminals at its headquarters and to try to get them to talk to one another.

## SO, THE FIRST FALTERING STEPS DOWN THE ROAD TO THE INTERNET WERE MADE.

The first message sent across the ARPANET took place in January 1969. It was meant to read 'Login'. But as the fragile pioneering system crashed after the first two letters, the very first Internet message actually said, "Lo"!

# ROBOTS

**A**s I said in the introduction to this section, the robots are coming. The second decade of the 21st century will see the rise of a robot army that will revolutionize our lives. Just in the same way that the Internet has shaken up the past ten years or so.

Or so says an American think-tank known as The Institute for the Future. They envisage robots coming to dominate everything, from the way we fight wars, to the way we organize our kitchens.

We've always been fascinated with the idea of creating life.

Mary Shelley does it in perhaps the most famous science fiction story of all, *Frankenstein*, which was first published anonymously in 1818. Before that, there were other stories and legends about the making of mechanical life. There are Greek myths full of attempts to make ancient types of robots: Pygmalion the sculptor fell in love with a statue he had brought to life, Daedalus used quicksilver to give voice to his statues, and Hephaestus the smith created an artificial man of bronze called Talos.

By medieval times a range of 'robots' had been imagined which mimicked both human and animal forms. Famous Italian all-rounder Leonardo da Vinci had used his research of the human body, which he had done to create his drawing *The Vitruvian Man*, to design a mechanical knight that could bust a few moves.

But it was in the 20th century that the robot was to fully mature in the minds of men.

Czech sci-fi author Karel Capek wrote a stage play in 1920 called *Rossum's Universal Robots*. It was one of the first visions of artificial humans, and history's first relevant use of the word robot. In Capek's story his robots are organic life, but they are made rather than born. They live a life of drudgery, which is why he used the name 'robota', as in Czech it means 'forced labour'.

## THE NAME ROBOT CAUGHT ON.

The Metal Maria created in the movie *Metropolis* in 1927 was called a robot, rather than automaton. And the same went for the 'annihilants' of Ming the Merciless in the *Flash Gordon* serials of the 1930s. But it was in books rather than films that robots really came to life.

American sci-fi writer Isaac Asimov came up with 'the Three Laws' of Robotics. First thought up in his 1942 story 'Runaround' the Three Laws were a set of rules that robots had to obey to ensure humans were never harmed.

## THE THREE LAWS:

1. A robot may not injure a human being or, through inaction, allow a human being to come to harm.

2. A robot must obey the orders given to it by human beings, except where such orders would conflict with the First Law.

3. A robot may not injure its own kind and defend its own kind unless it is interfering with the first or second rule.

## SO WHAT EXACTLY IS A ROBOT?

Science fiction gives us a model to use, but science itself can't quite make up its mind. In Japan, for example, they have a much more general idea of what makes a robot; a lot of automated machinery is thought to be robotic. But no one in the world is in any doubt about their newer household robots, like Asimo and Wakamaru.

## ROBOTS GET A BAD PRESS.

And it's no wonder. With a few cute exceptions such as R2D2, K9, Metal Mickey and WALL-E, robots have often been evil characters ever since *Metropolis*.

The US army is now making a four-legged pack robot called the BigDog. Guided by their own sensors, the BigDogs will be able to help in times of war, as air robot drones are helping stalk bombing targets overhead.

Thankfully, there are more positive uses of modern robots. In Japan and Korea, where many of the great robot inventors are likely to come from, attitudes to robots are more positive. And Google is working on robots cars that drive themselves. Once a technology is invented, it is very rare that it disappears.

**FOR GOOD, AND BAD, THE ROBOT IS YOUR FUTURE.**

# ROCKETS

**F**irst there was the firework. Many moons ago, long before the days of NASA, there lived a man named Wan-Hoo. Wan-Hoo was a minor Chinese official of the Ming Dynasty. He was also the world's first astronaut. **ALLEGEDLY.** Legend has it that, early in the 1500s, Wan figured he could launch himself into outer space. Cunningly using China's advanced firework technology to his advantage, Wan built his spaceship: a chair. To this chair Wan fastened 47 large rockets. Using what influence he could within the Dynasty, Wan called up 47 assistants. Each willing assistant, armed with a flaming torch, was charged with the task of rushing forward and lighting one of the long fuses.

On the day of lift-off the finely clothed Wan climbed onto his rocket chair and his 47 aides lit the fuses. The assistants hastily ran for cover. There was a tremendous roar and a huge explosion. The smoke cleared. The rocket chair was gone. **WAN WAS NEVER SEEN AGAIN.**

This tale was first reported, not in Chinese manuscripts, but in *Rockets and Jets*, a book written by American author Herbert S. Zim, in 1945. Only later was the story introduced into China. Nonetheless, the legend lives on. A crater on the far side of the Moon was named after Wan-Hoo, when the far side was first photographed in the 1960s.

For centuries after Wan-Hoo, writers and engineers grappled with the idea of propulsion. Propulsion is the force by which something such as a ship, a car, or a space rocket, is moved forward. Some of the early space voyage stories used very inventive methods of propulsion. So let's consider a few of the best ones.

As I mentioned in the introduction of the book, these early space stories come from a time, the 1600s, when astronomers had just found out that the Earth was in orbit around the Sun, and ships had started voyaging around the globe. So writers had already started to imagine sailing out into space four hundred years ago. Most of these first stories were about voyages to the Moon and how to get there. Hardly surprising really, since it's the nearest object to the Earth.

## Propelled by Demons

One example is *Somnium*. It is the first ever science fiction story and it was written in 1634 by German astronomer Johannes Kepler. In *Somnium* the hero of the story uses this method of propulsion: he is spirited away to the Moon by demons! Okay, not very scientific, especially from a man who worked out the laws of how the planets move around the Sun.

By the way, Johannes was a brilliant scientist but a rather poor teacher. Whenever he got excited, and he was almost always in this state, Johannes burst into speech without worrying about whether he was saying the right thing. In his first year of teaching he had only a small handful of students, and in his second, none whatsoever! He was the very picture of an absent-minded professor, delivering muddled lectures to an empty classroom.

## Propelled by Geese

Four years after *Somnium*, Francis Godwin wrote *The Man in the Moone*. The choice of propulsion in his tale was a bizarre flying machine made up of forty wild geese! The hero of the story harnesses himself to the geese but forgets that they migrate each year to the Moon – come on, we've all done it. So, instead of ending up at his destination, he finds himself in space. When you hear people talk about a 'wild goose chase' to describe a useless pursuit, remember that the saying comes from the time of this story about a trip to the Moon.

## Propelled by Water

But perhaps my favourite method of propulsion in these early space stories goes to the legendary swashbuckling French swordsman with a large snout, Cyrano de Bergerac. Cyrano's story used a most unusual means of getting to the Moon. Now, it is well known that the Sun seems to 'draw up' dewdrops. What actually happens is the sunlight turns the dew water into gas, but Cyrano imagined that dewdrops might be used for flight. So he got his hero to trap plenty of dew in bottles, strapped the bottles to his waist, simply stood around in sunlight, and up he went! Pure genius, though not really possible.

These early stories might seem a bit daft to us now, but they made a lasting impression on science. The world's oldest science organisation is the Royal Society in London, set up in 1660, and John Wilkins, another bishop, wrote one of their first books. Inspired by the above stories, he saw space travel as a very real possibility, sometime in the future.

# Try This at Home

## BUILDING YOUR OWN ROCKET

It wasn't until 1881 that Russian rocket pioneer Nikolai Kibalchich finally came up with the principle of the modern rocket. He dreamt up the method as he waited in prison to be executed for the assassination of Alexander II, the Russian emperor. This was his idea: propulsion by slow burning gas which escapes through a nozzle, the narrow end of the rocket.

And it's using this very same method that you can build your own rocket, from an empty Coke or lemonade plastic bottle and a tablet of Alka-Seltzer®.

### THIS IS HOW IT WORKS:

• The bottle is partly filled with water and the Alka-Seltzer® tablet

• Gas pressure builds up inside the bottle and expels the water, creating the thrust to accelerate the rocket, which is greater than both the air resistance and the weight of the rocket

• The rocket blasts high into the air. Some homemade rockets reach maximum speeds of 200 km/h. The world record height is more than 300 metres!

# BIG BROTHER

**E**ver had the feeling that someone is listening in? Maybe they're reading your texts and emails, or listening to your phone calls. They could even be following you down the street.

Well, they did all this and more in the nightmare society of spying and surveillance written about in 1948 by British author George Orwell in his book *Nineteen Eighty-Four*. The story is about a big government gone mad with lust for power, and the head of that government is Big Brother.

**BIG BROTHER BRAKE IS WATCHING YOU**

He's as famous as Frankenstein and reads your mind through his 'Thought Police'. His realm is 'Room 101'.

George Orwell's masterpiece was an inspiration. Not only to the many movie-makers who wanted to portray a world where everyone is spied upon, but also because the title of Orwell's book has become a kind of shorthand for anything that seems to threaten our free and open society.

Some people think that Orwell's Big Brother vision is coming true. In Orwell's book there was *Newspeak*. *Newspeak* is a controlled and dishonest language used by the media, that limits free thought and stops people thinking for themselves. You can see similar things in our society today.

```
War is now often called conflict.
 Civilian casualties of war are
  described as collateral damage.
Sacking people from their jobs is
         known as right-sizing.
  A fix for a software bug is a
     reliability enhancement.
```

Big Brother's second weapon of control is the 'Thought Police'; they use technology to tell people what to think. In *Nineteen Eighty-Four* there is enough wealth for everyone to be free and happy, but inequality is kept as a way of controlling people. The 'Thought Police' use 'telescreens' as an all-seeing eye. Every day you are encouraged to exercise in front of the telescreen, but as you watch the screen, the screen watches *you*.

Something similar has happened recently in our society; it's been discovered that spying agencies have been watching what everyone does on the Internet. As you surf on different websites, they watch you. As you email your friend, they watch you. As you text your mates, they watch you. It seems that the only place you can have a free and private conversation is on top of a mountain. And even then you can never be sure; what about space satellite surveillance?!

The telescreens are a bit like today's CCTV. They were first invented by the Nazis during World War II to keep an eye on the launch of V2 rockets. Today there are as many as 4.2 million CCTV cameras in the UK alone. That's one CCTV camera for every fourteen people – making the UK the world's most spied on society.

One CCTV company in England has developed a CCTV camera that can communicate with offenders on the spot. And an American company is using sense-through-the-wall technology that can detect breathing and heart rates from outside a building by picking up on the radio waves that humans emit. As envisaged in Steven Spielberg's *The Minority Report* (2002), it will soon be possible to scan shoppers as they enter stores. And as suggested in *Enemy of the State*, a 1998 movie starring Will Smith, our spending habits, our location, our every movement and conversation, are visible to others whose motives we cannot know.

Isn't all this a bit worrying for a free and open society like ours? It seems not. In opinion polls in the US and the

UK around 75% of people want *more*, not less, surveillance. We have won the victory over ourselves.

We love
Big Brother!

# FLYING CARS

**S**ome people are never happy, are they?

*"The future we were promised hasn't really arrived"*, they say. According to them, we're now meant to be living in a world of silver flame-retardant jumpsuits, ray guns, and x-ray specs. No doubt we're also meant to be invisible and immortal by now too.

Some go even further. They believe the time has come to hold science fiction to task, saying, *"This may be a world of cool technologies but, dude, where's my flying car?"* There really is no pleasing some people.

It's certainly true that few machines symbolize the future like the flying car.

It has made popular appearances in futuristic TV cartoons, such as the 1960s animation, *The Jetsons*. In cinema, too, the flying car has been seen chittying along in movies such as *Chitty Chitty Bang Bang* (1968), *Blade Runner* (1982), *Back to the Future 1 & 2* (1985, 1989), *The Fifth Element* (1997), and the *Harry Potter* series (2001–2011). Indeed, the earliest story equipped with a flying car was probably Jules Verne's *Master of the World* (1904). Verne's car not only flew, it could also double as a boat or submarine. **SORTED**.

By 1928 Henry Ford had realised the concept in real life. But the first attempts with Ford's 'sky flivver' were troubled; a pilot died in an early test flight. In 1956 cruise missile engineer Moulton Taylor unveiled the 'Aerocar'. Cruising up to 100mph, the little yellow car proved far more impractical than its fictional versions.

And that's always been the problem with the flying car. It's technically doable, but tricky in practice.

There can be no time more deserving than today for the introduction of the flying car, in our world full of traffic jams. Take China, for instance. September 2013 saw the world's longest traffic jam, more than 100km long and lasting for weeks. The problem is so common in China that some people have seen it as a business opportunity. Their motorbike business will weave its way between the gridlocked lanes and take you to the destination you were meant to be going to. Heck, they'll even provide someone to sit in your car for you until the jam is over, if it ever ends.

Pizza deliveries to jammed cars are also very common. Pizza express, even if the traffic isn't.

## THIS IS CLEARLY GETTING RIDICULOUS.

In the *Doctor Who* episode, *Gridlock*, the Doctor takes his new companion Martha Jones to the far distant future of flying cars, where they encounter the traffic jam from hell – not weeks or months, but years!

With a host of factors outside our control, no wonder people still dream of the freedom of the sky, made possible by the flying car. A 2010 MSNBC poll in the USA found that 90% of the country would buy a flying car if given the chance.

The latest real-life model is the futuristic 'Skycar M400', invented by Paul Moller, who has been trying to perfect the flying car for over fifty years. The Moller Skycar has a vertical, helicopter-like take-off and landing, smooth flight, and comfortable drive. It mostly transports four people, but single-seat and six-seat versions are also planned. It sounds sci-fi in its completeness.

So what's the problem?

Well, firstly, one of these babies would cost you half a million dollars! That's a lot of pocket money. Not only that, but every time a public demo has been announced, it's been swiftly cancelled. It seems that, fifty years on, the flying car is the best real world example of 'vapourware', a name the computer industry gives to a product that is announced to the public but never actually released. In this world of sustainability, fuel costs, and air traffic control, we're still some way off those mesmerising skylines full of flivvers.

## SO, DUDE, WHERE'S MY FLYING CAR?!

# LIGHTSABERS

**S**urely it's the coolest weapon of all time?

Scottish actor Ewan McGregor thought so. He was so excited at being asked to play Obi-Wan Kenobi in the *Star Wars* prequels that he confessed to practicing his lightsaber technique whilst making the energetic laser *THHHHHHWWWWOM!* noises himself!

The lightsaber is associated with the Jedi Knights. It's an elegant weapon consisting of a cylindrical hilt, a blade formed from a tight loop of highly focused light about one metre long, and when powered up emits a coloured blade of pure energy. It is essentially a laser of immense power. And it's able to penetrate and cut most solid materials with little resistance, except for another lightsaber blade, of course.

The closest science has come to a lightsaber is the plasma gun. Plasma guns are used to coat surfaces with thin films and in the construction of aircraft engines. They work by blasting large volumes of gas through an electric arc. This energizes the gas to a plasma state, dividing it into positively charged ions and loose electrons. Plasma radiates brilliant light and heat. But the electrons continue to be attracted to the ions. They re-attach themselves as soon as the energy diminishes, which makes plasma unstable. Sadly, that makes it tricky.

In late 2013 boffins in the United States said they had found a way to make light particles bind together to form a new molecule that behaves almost exactly like George Lucas' deadly devices.

With a new trilogy of *Star Wars* films on the way, are boffins busy building away in time for Christmas 2015, when *Star Wars* fans worldwide will be able to buy their own lightsabers?

# TOP 10 ROBOTS

"skwee-tweep-tweep-blip-di-blip-swark-kikiki-peep-peep-whooOOOooo pweep... brrrrrripp."

## 1 Marvin The Paranoid Android

*Claim to fame: from the radio plays, books, and film of* The Hitchhikers Guide to the Galaxy, *Marvin is a kind of robotic version of Eeyore from* Winnie the Pooh.

ROBOTIC CHARM: brain the size of a planet, Marvin is an updated 1950s retro-robot, and it's not so much that he's paranoid as a little down in spirit. After all, only a small fraction of his huge brain is being occupied with something useful.

## 2 R2D2

*Claim to fame: does he really need an introduction?! Okay, he's the cute robot in* Star Wars *who looks like the swing-bin from your kitchen. How's that?*

ROBOTIC CHARM: probably the first robot to hit our movie screens who actually has attitude and cuteness. SwingBin, sorry, R2D2 communicates through whistles and hoots. He also hacks gigantic space stations that can destroy planets.

## 3 WALL-E

*Claim to fame: the rubbish-collecting robot created by Pixar, WALL-E is left to clean up the world after the humans have left it trashed.*

ROBOTIC CHARM: taking SwingBin's cuteness to another level, Wall-E not only protects the environment, he also falls in love with another robot.

## 4 T-800 (The Terminator)

*Claim to fame: the assassinating robot from the future, in the* Terminator *film series.*

ROBOTIC CHARM: he starts off as an ice-cold killing machine and ends up as a child saving hero with a heart of gold. "Hasta la vista, baby!"

## 5 Optimus Prime

*Claim to fame: leader of the Autobots in the* Transformers *franchise.*

ROBOTIC CHARM: he's only charming if you like Viking heroes masquerading as an alien robot masquerading as a giant truck.

# 6 Gort

*Claim to fame: from the movie* The Day the Earth Stood Still *and its 2008 remake.*

ROBOTIC CHARM: an eight-foot, metal robot from a distant planet who comes to Earth aboard a flying saucer, doesn't speak, but shoots deadly beams from his single eye. COOL!

# 7 Sonny

*Claim to fame: the robot who defeated the three laws of robotics in the movie* I, Robot.

ROBOTIC CHARM: Sonny looks so much like he was designed by Apple it's a wonder they didn't call the movie iRobot.

# 8 False Maria

*Claim to fame: the female robot from the 1927 (yes, 1927!) movie* Metropolis.

ROBOTIC CHARM: the sleek, cool, metallic and arty-looking Maria is one of cinema's most iconic images.

# 9 Robot

*Claim to fame: OK, not the best of names, but he's the robot in the* Lost in Space *franchise.*

ROBOTIC CHARM: looks a little like the robot from *Forbidden Planet* (he has the same designer), Robot was one of TV's first robots and even had his own catchphrase, "Danger! Will Robinson! Danger!"

# 10 K-9

*Claim to fame: smart-alec robotic mutt that proved for many actors on* Doctor Who *that working with animals wasn't so unpredictable.*

ROBOTIC CHARM: the only dog in our top 10, K-9 had a laser in his nose, even though the Doctor has always been against weapons. K-9's control system was so unreliable it often used to interfere with the television studio cameras. And, like the old version of the Daleks, K-9 had some difficulty with flights of stairs.

# TOP 10
## ANDROIDS

Robots designed to look and feel like humans were always going to be a bit weird and creepy.

## 1 Roy Batty

*Claim to fame: the wonderfully superhuman villain-android-replicant from the movie* Blade Runner.

ROBOTIC CHARM: leader of the Nexus-6 replicants, Roy is very intelligent, handsome, dashing, and deadly. The scenes in the film where he comes to terms with his emotions steal the movie. Shame about the silly name; he sounds like a guy who runs a fish-and-chip shop. But still our number one.

## 2 David-8

*Claim to fame: the most sophisticated movie android of them all, from the movie* Prometheus. *Heck, David even has his own website: http://www.weylandindustries.com/david*

ROBOTIC CHARM: so human he even styles his hair to look like a movie star. You'll have a job trying to work out whether he's good, as he tends to do evil things out of scientific curiosity. Typical boffin. David 8 is guaranteed to

149

surprise you. Keep your eyes peeled.

## 3  T-1000 Terminator

*Claim to fame: the liquid metal fella from* Terminator 2.

**ROBOTIC CHARM:** an incredible fighting machine but with a very limited emotional range – definitely not a touchy-feely kind of guy. He has a great confused, does-not-compute face when he starts to malfunction, as if he is asking himself: *"How can someone as perfect as me fail?!"*

## 4  Ash

*Claim to fame: the quiet and unassuming science officer from the movie* Alien.

**ROBOTIC CHARM:** Ash is so convincing at being human that the crew don't even realize he's an android until he starts to go haywire. It turns out he's acting on secret orders: "Bring back the alien life form. Crew expendable."

## 5  Andrew

*Claim to fame: domestic android in the film* Bicentennial Man.

**ROBOTIC CHARM:** arty, sensitive, and funny, Andrew's life as an android sees him evolve from a 'tin man' on a two-century journey to become more human than most human beings.

## 6 Jordan Two Delta

*Claim to fame: the clone supermodel android from the movie* Island.

**ROBOTIC CHARM:** Jordan Two Delta is a clone of a Calvin Klein supermodel in the movie, but she is merely being kept alive for spare parts, just in case her real life counterpart loses a limb or two. Jordan falls in love with another android and, understandably, runs away from the 'island', showing intelligence and genuine emotion.

## 7 Data

*Claim to fame: one of the officers on board USS Enterprise in* Star Trek.

**ROBOTIC CHARM:** Data aimed to become more human in his behavior, often with amusing results. He looked a little like an anemic football manager and over the course of the series became more human-like due to an emotion chip inserted into his positronic brain.

## 8 Bishop

*Claim to fame: executive officer onboard the main spaceship in the movie* Aliens.

**ROBOTIC CHARM:** he does a lightning fast knife trick, cuts his finger by mistake and reveals his blood is white. That's the first hint the crew get he's not real. He's otherwise good at his job until he's torn in two by an alien. That's got to hurt, even if you are an android.

## 9.  David

*Claim to fame: the child-robot from Steven Spielberg's* A. I. Artificial Intelligence.

**ROBOTIC CHARM:** like some kind of CGI'd Pinocchio, David (why are they so often called David?!) may be the saddest android of the bunch. Created to love without question, David is abandoned by the mother who bought him as a substitute for her real son. The film is brilliant in the way it makes you feel for a mere machine.

## IO Gunslinger

*Claim to fame: the amusement park leisure cowboy from the movie* Westworld.

**ROBOTIC CHARM:**  you've seen all those robot movies. Be honest, is it really a good idea to wander into an amusement park and play cowboys with real gunslinging robots? With live ammo?! That's what happens in *Westworld*. It doesn't end well. **THE GUNSLINGER IS THE ORIGINAL 'TERMINATOR'.**

# TOP 10
## SCI-FI VEHICLES

## 1 Tumbler Batmobile

*Claim to fame: the iconic car from the Christopher Nolan trilogy of* Batman *movies.*

**FAST FACTOIDS:** the Batmobile has taken many forms since the *Batman* TV series in the 1960s. But it was with Nolan's 2005 black ops take on the vehicle that the Tumbler transformed the Batmobile into a military-minded machine kitted out with autocannons, rocket launcher, and tank-like armour. Heck, it even made Batman look cool, and he still wears tights.

## 2 Anakin Skywalker's Podracer

*Claim to fame: Anakin's podracer first appeared in the 1999* Stars Wars *movie* The Phantom Menace.

**FAST FACTOIDS:** an awesome vehicle when you consider it was built by a nine-year-old slave out of spare engine parts. Capable of speeds of 588mph (curious that a planet in a distant galaxy should use Earthly measures of speed), it became the fastest podracer in the galaxy (it says here). Not really a car, but I don't care. It's going in the list as it's so cool, and I have fond memories of the podracer video game. AND it made the coolest vehicle noise in movie history.

# 3 The DeLorean DMC-12

*Claim to fame: the cool time-travelling car from the* Back to the Future *trilogy.*

FAST FACTOIDS: who would have thought that one of the coolest ever sci-fi vehicles started off in a car factory in 1980s Belfast? Doc Emmett Brown's legendary nuclear-powered time machine is not only one of the ultimate sci-fi cars, but there are still around 6,500 DMC-12s in existence, so you could actually go out and get one! Let me know if the flux capacitor works...

# 4 Flying Taxicab

*Claim to fame: from the under-rated and visually beautiful movie* The Fifth Element *by French film director Luc Besson.*

FAST FACTOIDS: the flying taxicab featured in one of the coolest vertical/horizontal car chases in history as cabbie Bruce Willis is chased through the polluted air of a futuristic New York by hovering police cars, proving along the way that you never really learn to swear until you learn to drive. Or in this case, hover.

# 5 Police Spinner

*Claim to fame: the cop cars from the movie* Blade Runner *(1982).*

**FAST FACTOIDS:** unlike a real cop car, as these things take off vertically from standstill. Believe it or not, I've actually seen this beauty in real life. It sits in a sci-fi museum in Seattle. Sadly, I wasn't able to test its flying capabilities. But remember, there is an art to flying. The knack lies in learning how to throw yourself at the ground and miss.

# 6 Lexus 2054

*Claim to fame: the sleek futuristic auto-drive from* The Minority Report *movie (2002).*

**FAST FACTOIDS:** Lexus, the luxury vehicle division of Japanese auto giants Toyota, are said to have paid $5 million to get the 2054 concept car in the movie. In the movie it could also fly. If this is the kind of car cops are driving in the future, they must have had some salary rise.

# 7 Audi RSQ

*Claim to fame: the tireless silver Audi from* I, Robot *(2004).*

**FAST FACTOIDS:** it had wheels but no tyres, and seemed to float above the road before Will Smith wrecked it in the movie.

## 8 SoroSuub X-34 Landspeeder

*Claim to fame: the wonderfully beat-up flying car of Luke Skywalker in* Star Wars.

**FAST FACTOIDS:** more like a hovercar than anything else, Luke's Landspeeder may lack ion cannons and maximum thrust, but its simple charm in the first ever *Star Wars* movie stole the hearts of many. And it could 'cruise' at 155mph!

## 9 Optimus Prime

*Claim to fame: leader of the Autobots in the* Transformers *franchise.*

**FAST FACTOIDS:** this is meant to be a *cool* list, right? So what's cooler than a truck that transforms into the leader of a robotic race engaged in a civil war that's been raging for millions of years? Come to think of it, maybe Optimus should be in the top 3 of our list?! **NAH.**

## 10 Light Cycle

*Claim to fame: the 'motorbike' from the* Tron *franchise.*

**FAST FACTOIDS:** powered by liquid energy (I think that means petrol, tbh), the five generations of light cycle from the *Tron* movies become ever cooler, and show that even in the future only bikers understand why dogs love to stick their heads out of car windows.

**S**cience fiction didn't invent monsters. Monsters have always been part of the tall tales that humans tell. Yet sci-fi has been able to put a modern and scientific spin on many of the monsters from our dark and misty past. Weird wolf-men, such as Professor Remus Lupin in *Harry Potter* and Oz in *Buffy the Vampire Slayer*, are now the victims of a disease known as lycanthropy. The hordes of zombies that drag their feet across modern movie screens are the result of viruses leaked from a mad doctor's lab.

Even Mother Nature herself can become monstrous. That's why we have stories about giant apes scaling skyscrapers, severe weather that could spell the end of days, and flocks of angry birds intent on some mysterious revenge.

Yet, sci-fi's greatest monster is us: the monster that looks back at us when we gaze into the mirror. It was Charles Darwin and Alfred Russel Wallace who first came up with the idea of the theory of evolution. Evolution is an explanation of how living things change over many generations, but it's also a theory that can be used to wonder what might become of humans in the future.

When sci-fi uses evolution with a glance to the past, it often has qualms about the creature that lurks within us. Modern man might think he is very civilized, but when you strip away the layers of civility, underneath skulks a monster waiting to erupt. That's the idea in Robert Louis Stevenson's famous sci-fi story *The Strange Case of Dr Jekyll and Mr Hyde*. Many other books and movies also remind us that the appearance of progress and civilization is a fragile mask covering up a creature beneath.

## BUT MONSTERS ARE NOT JUST DARK.

When sci-fi uses evolution with an eye to the future, it can summon up superheroes. Rippling muscles at the ready, armed with laser vision and super-strength (though sadly often attired in tights), these super men and women are icons of our own future. You could become super by a quirk of nature, like Spiderman or the X-Men. Or, through gadgets, you could pop on some kind of super-suit and vanquish the villains, as Batman and Iron Man do. Superheroes represent dreams of how humans can overcome obstacles and deal with danger. They can also be easily persuaded to give you a lecture on how naughtiness never wins and how heroes can be relied upon to defeat the monsters.

So, within the pages of our Monster section you will find entries on monsters such as cyborgs, mutants, and superheroes. Here too you will find some real-life developments that could turn us into monsters: eugenics, cloning, and genetic engineering. You'll see that some of the most far-fetched things that have happened in today's world were anticipated. Once more, the sci-fi of our past predicted much of the present and possibly some of our future.

And as the relentless march of the monster continues, remember you read it here first!

# EUGENICS

The world seems to be full of self-help books giving you advice on how to improve yourself.

Maybe they think you need more exercise, flabhead. Perhaps you need to read more books, game girl. Or maybe it's just a case of cutting down on visits to the local burger bar, scoff chops.

The topic of eugenics is about improving the human race as a whole through bloodlines. Funny word, eugenics. The 'eu' bit is Greek and means 'good', the 'gen' bit refers to 'birth' or 'race'. So you can see that together it suggests improving the quality of the human population.

It sounds okay, but the trouble is that eugenics has a history of *very* dodgy ideas. Many people into eugenics argue against the mixing of races, which is known as miscegenation. A good fictional example of this can be found in the *Harry Potter* books. The Death Eater wizards believe that they are superior to all other races and argue against miscegenation, using the insult 'mudbloods' for those with no magical ancenstry, which include Harry's friend, Hermione.

## EUGENICS HAS A HORRIBLE HISTORY.

When people realised humans inherited traits from their

ancestors, they began to come up with ideas to 'improve' the human race. Take Greek philosopher Plato, for example. In his 360 BC book *The Republic* Plato argued that a good way to improve humans was to kill inferior babies at birth. Hardly a vote winner! Plato was, thankfully, opposed by another Greek boffin called Hippocrates (the founder of medicine), whose Hippocratic Oath is still taken by doctors today.

An early science fiction book *Gulliver's Travels* was the first to explore what a society based on eugenics would look like. The book was written way back in 1726 by Irish writer Jonathan Swift. At one point in the story, Gulliver arrives in the land of the Houyhnhnms. These creatures, identical to horses, run a eugenics programme involving the selective breeding of their human slaves, known as 'yahoos'. At first Gulliver is mistaken for one of the yahoos. But he manages to convince the horse masters that he is intelligent enough to be saved. If he hadn't spoken up, Gulliver would have been sacrificed as part of their cruel eugenics programme.

When *Gulliver's Travels* was written, improving human bloodlines wasn't known as eugenics. The word was coined by Francis Galton, the cousin of Charles Darwin. Galton believed in the inequality of humans. For example, he thought Africans were inferior and suggested that the east coast of Africa be settled by the Chinese, who were, according to Galton, superior.

But the most chilling supporters of eugenics were the Nazis, during the 1930s and 40s. The Nazis forced hundreds of thousands of men, women, and children to be sterilized, to prevent them from passing on their genes. Much of the horror of the Nazis regime was predicted in a 1937 science fiction book called *Swastika Night*, by British writer Katherine Burdekin. In her future history, Burdekin imagined that the Nazis would come to dominate the world and force their ideas of inequality on the human race. *Swastika Night* almost came true. But thankfully for us all, the world pulled together and the Nazis were defeated, along with their breeding programmes and genocide.

# MUTANTS

**W**ant to hear a weird story about Charles Darwin?
Well, one day, old Charlie read a report on a family of
hairy humans. Now I don't just mean *slightly* hairy; I mean
their bodies were *entirely covered* in hair from head to furry
foot, you know, so hairy that you could comb their face! As
a result of this unusual look, four generations of these hairy
persons had been kept for amusement at the royal court in
Burma.

Clearly, Charlie pondered, there was a quality in these
people that, unlike all those around them, made them keep
on being hairy. Very hairy!

History tells us other examples of difference in human
form. Conjoined twins, for instance, which are identical
twins born fused together. Or those affected by cyclopia,
being born with one eye, like Homer's famous monster from
ancient times. Or those suffering from sirenomelia, where
the lower limbs are fused together, also known as
'mermaid's syndrome'.

## MUTANTS, ONE AND ALL.

Darwin helped discover that mutation lies at the heart of
nature. Without mutant forms, none of the plants and
animals on planet Earth would exist.

It's too easy to dismiss mutants as monsters when, of course, we are *all* mutants. How we may mutate in the future is one of science fiction's keenest obsessions. In his book *The Time Machine*, HG Wells thought that the difference between social classes in England would become so great that the classes would evolve into different species of human, each a mutant in its own way.

One of those mutant human forms was the underground-dwelling Morlocks. Wells described them as being 'ape-like', with little or no clothing, large eyes, and grey fur covering their bodies. The Morlocks were one of science fiction's very first mutants.

A far more recent mutant is The Hulk. Mutants such as him are often known as 'strong mutants', as they usually become mutated through some fast-tracked way, rather than normal evolution. In the case of The Hulk it's because he was exposed to gamma radiation. In the case of the X-Men it's because they have an 'X-gene' which normal humans don't have and which gives mutants their abilities. It also seems that the mutations happened because of exposure to radiation.

## PERHAPS THE MOST FAMOUS MUTANTS OF ALL ARE THE DALEKS.

Now, we have to be careful about this. The Daleks themselves, including their outer tank-like robotic shells, are actually CYBORGS, as you will see elsewhere in the book. But the squidgy alien creatures *inside* the robot shells, the Kaleds, are **MUTANTS!** The Kaleds, a race of extraterrestrials from the planet Skaro, were deliberately made into strong mutants by the villainous scientist Davros. His final modification, or mutation, was to take away their ability to feel pity for other creatures. In other words he turned them into the uncaring monsters they are. The Daleks are the dark side of mutation. They soon came to see themselves as the supreme race in the universe and began their conquest of domination and extermination.

How mutant humans will turn out is another matter. Earthly boffins have begun experimenting on mutant forms of the zebrafish. Using radiation, chemicals, or viruses, boffins make mutant forms of these innocent and colourful little creatures, just to see what happens. One experiment resulted in producing a little fish that exploded when exposed to light.

What a very Dalek thing to do. Or maybe an experiment that would definitely get Davros' approval.

# SUPERHEROES

[Stage direction: Batman and Robin are on a mission, solving the latest dastardly crime, when Robin asks Batman about the history of superheroes.]

"Holy cow, Batman!   What does the future hold for humans?   What will humans, one day, become?"   asked Robin.

"These are very modern questions, Robin," replied Batman. "Time was when people didn't worry about the future.   But then along came Charles Darwin and Alfred Russel Wallace with their theory of evolution, and [KAPOW!] ever since the fertile brains of fiction writers, movie makers, and artists, have been busy worrying about it."

"Touché, Batman! But who invented the superman?!"   [BASH!]

"Ah, Robin, the superman was invented by German boffin Friedrich Nietzsche (pronounced 'Knee-cheh').   He'd come up with the idea of the Übermensch ('super-man', 'over-man', or 'super-human') in his 1883 book Thus Spoke *Zarathustra* (even I am not going to try to

pronounce that, Robin). Nietzsche's notion of
the übermensch was of humans looking to better
themselves and evolve to a higher state."

[THWACK!] "No other symbol in sci-fi has
changed as dramatically as the 'super-man',
Robin. Early ideas in comic books were really
just about wanting to fly, or wanting to shoot
bullets out of your butt. And the heroes often
wore silly costumes with Y-fronts outside their
tights, Robin."

"Holy satire, Batman, I'm not sure what you
mean," said Robin, defensively.

"Don't worry, Robin, today's superhero is
far more sophisticated. Today we are more like
anti-heroes. Moviegoers see superheroes as
symbols of human evolution and our fears about
science."

"GULP! That's a huge responsibility, Batman.
Thank heavens there are so MANY of us,"
reflected Robin.

"Yes, my cape crusading chum, 21st century
cinema seems to be full of 'over-men' like us,
but superhero fiction began in 1938 with
Superman. Since then superheroes have broken
into radio, TV, and books, and are top of the
pops in modern CGI movies.

[BIFF!] But unlike heroes of the past, such as Tarzan or Zorro, modern superheroes are a different breed. Guys like us and Iron Man are highly skilled, with easy access to super-scientific gadgetry. Other superheroes have superhuman powers which they get from some chance interaction with a scientific world, like Captain America and The Hulk.

"Holy mutants, Batman! What about the others?" said Robin. [THUNK!]

"Well, my friend, Superman is an alien. He gets his power from the fact that he was born on the planet of Krypton. Spiderman got his superpowers from being bitten by a radioactive arachnid. And Thor and Loki are actually Gods!"

"But, Batman! What if superheroes became super-villains instead? What then would happen to the world? Who would police the police, and who would watch the Watchmen?" said Robin.

[ZONK!] "An excellent question, my crime-fighting fellow! Some of the superheroes in later comics ask the same questions. Frank Miller's: *The Dark Knight Returns* (1986) and Alan Moore's *Watchmen* (1986-7) wonder what society might be like if science gave us all superhero status. Would mere mortals get fed up of fighting crime? Would the temptation to commit crime themselves prove too great? What if you could become invisible? Would you be tempted to sneak around giving people wedgies, just for a laugh?"

"Holy complex futures, Batman!" said Robin.

[Stage direction: having saved the day as usual, the dynamic duo retire to the Batcave to think more about plotting to keep the future out of the hands of amateur crime-fighters.]

# CLONING

**H**istory is full of the idea of copies.

We've been thinking of simulations of ourselves since ancient times all the way through to images we upload onto modern video games. One ancient idea, and a rather creepy one, is that of the **DOPPELGÄNGER**. This is a spirit that looks just like us and is usually just seen before your death! Mary Shelley, the author of *Frankenstein*, wrote that her husband, the famous poet Percy Shelley, had seen his Doppelgänger two weeks before drowning. **GULP.**

Boffins say that clones have existed for a long time. Identical human twins are clones. They're made when a single fertilized egg divides into two separate embryos. But, whereas clones are exact copes, twins are not. Their genes are totally the same, but their appearances and their characters differ. Stories of twins have also been famous through the years. The founders of Rome in 770 BC are said to be the twins Romulus and Remus. Romulus is meant to have killed his brother, an action that may have led to our fascination with the 'evil twin'.

The idea of evil twins became popular in early movies. One famous example involved British comic actor Charlie Chaplin. In the 1940 anti-Nazi movie *The Great Dictator*, Chaplin plays a poor Jewish barber who is a dead ringer (we might even say Doppelgänger) for Adenoid Hynckel, a hilarious caricature of Adolf Hitler. Once science fiction had begun to explore the idea of human cloning, movies about clones, rather than twins became more common. The 1978 film, *The Boys from Brazil*, is a good example. And no, it's not about The World Cup. It's about a mad doctor and his attempt to clone Hitler and set up a fourth Reich (Hitler's evil lot were known as The Third Reich).

In real life boffins got to work on cloning animals first.

Only a few years before an actual animal clone was made, US author Michael Crichton had written *Jurassic Park*. Like Mary Shelley's *Frankenstein* before it, *Jurassic Park* was a warning to boffins not to mess around with nature. Written in 1990, with the famous movie coming three years later, *Jurassic Park* is about dinosaurs, of course. But the famous theme park monsters were *cloned* dinosaurs, and their creation by scientists leads to all kinds of unforeseen chaos. Well, there was *one* scientist who foresaw it, a mathematician, but nobody listened to him. PFFT.

On 5th July 1996 the first ever artificially cloned mammal was born.

Dolly the sheep was made of DNA taken from a grown-up female sheep's teat. The breed they used was a Finn Dorset sheep, but the name Dolly came from the famous American country and western singer Dolly Parton, who is also famous for her teats. Cloning animals may help preserve endangered species and may also help those researching the cloning of human tissue.

If human cloning is achieved in the future, would it benefit everyone or only those rich enough to afford it?

A theme that comes up a lot in fiction is the idea of using clones as a supply of organs for transplants. The 2010 movie *Never Let Me Go* is set in an alternative history where human clones are created to provide organs for naturally born humans, despite the fact that the clones are living, breathing humans themselves.

And clones have also made an important appearance in the *Star Wars* universe. *The Clone Wars* is about the use of clones to quickly make a well-trained and disposable army which is more adaptive than the droids (autonomous robots) used by the enemy. This sounds much like the Sontarans in *Doctor Who*. They too are clones, reproduced to make the best army possible.

As Mary Shelley once said, technology is a two-edged sword; it can be used for both good and bad.

# GENETIC ENGINEERING

Is it wrong to design a baby?

Scientists may soon be able to design new human beings. By altering the genetic makeup, or DNA, in a living human cell, these boffins will be able to choose what sort of human being we become.

Not much can be done at the moment, but soon scientists will be able to decide on our hair or eye colour, or even how brainy and beautiful babies are. But should boffins be allowed to do this? Is it a good idea to monkey around with molecules? Well, as you can probably guess, science fiction stories have been asking these sorts of questions for many years.

Back in 1896 HG Wells (yes, *him* again) wrote a story called *The Island of Dr Moreau*. Dr Moreau is one of those mad doctors of the movies. In Wells' tale Moreau is secretly doing experiments with the aim of changing animals into humans. Yes, *I* know it's a bad idea, and *you* know it's a bad idea, but that doesn't seem to occur to boffins like Moreau. Even though he had good intentions (he wanted to create a race of humans with no cruelty), the end result is predictably bad [SPOILER!]: a race of half-creatures, or chimera, lurking in the island's jungles (it's no wonder

*Jurassic Park* also took place on an island).

*The Island of Dr Moreau* was the most famous example of early stories about the planned 'engineering' of living creatures. By 1924, fact followed fiction when British biologist JBS Haldane foresaw our genetic future. His essay *Daedalus, or Science and the Future* predicted a day when boffins would engineer a solution to the world's food problem. His essay also talked about modified children born from artificial wombs, which were supposed to result in an improvement of the human race.

# THEN CAME *BRAVE NEW WORLD*.

This is a famous novel written in 1932 by British writer Aldous Huxley. In *Brave New World*, Huxley took the idea of modified children a step further. In his book, embryos are engineered for life as 'alphas', 'betas' or 'gammas', and they are slotted into a structure where they stay for life. There is no war, no poverty and no pain, but humans seem to have been robbed of their humanity and individuality.

By the 1950s the code of life was cracked, DNA was deciphered and since then genetic engineering has made rapid progress. Science fiction writers have kept pace with science. They understand what goes on in real labs.

One of those writers was Michael Crichton. He was the guy who wrote *Jurassic Park*, but he also wrote a book all about our genetic future called *Next* (2006). The book is a techno-thriller that explores a world dominated by science, greed, and legal battles. *Next* is about a talking ape. It features politicians and businessmen who spend billions each year on genetic engineering. The book follows a genetic boffin as he produces a transgenic ape. The ape has some human features but also the mind of a young child. The ape's 'family' struggle to raise him as they attempt to hide the true nature of the ape's genetic makeup from friends and neighbours.

## IS THIS OUR FUTURE?

A bizarre world of gene-stealing boffins and businessmen, meddling with things that some of us think should be left well alone? Only time will tell. But it does seem, once again, that old HG Wells is on the way to making a pretty accurate prediction.

# MIND CONTROL

**Y**ou're sat in a school classroom as the teacher waffles on incessantly about the levels of manganese production in Kazakhstan, or something.

Don't you wish you could stop him? That you could control his brain, and make him stick his head in a bucket of cold custard? He may still waffle, of course, but now it's just a pleasant set of gurgling custard noises, as you and your classmates while away your time playing on your phone/tablet/iPad.

## WELL, YOU'RE NOT ALONE.

The obsession with controlling the minds of others was all the rage in the United States, following the discoveries of French egghead Franz Anton Mesmer, early in the nineteenth century. Mesmer discovered what he called animal magnetism (mesmerism). The evolution of his ideas and practices led to the development in 1842 of hypnosis: the ability to hypnotise, or 'mesmerise', other people.

Many science fiction tales have featured mind control, both through natural and artificial means. Ford McCormick's *March Hare Mission* (1951) imagined a mind control drug, called nepenthal, which wiped clean the receiver's short-term memory – very handy for dealing with boring teachers. You could slip it into their mug of tea at break-time.

Arthur C. Clarke described a mechanical method for manipulating the mind in *Patent Pending*, a 1954 story that talked about the recording of memory and thoughts for later use. Jurassic Park inventor Michael Crichton wrote a book called *The Terminal Man* in 1972, which experimented with a similar idea. The novel's neuroscientists attempt brain control through electrode implants.

In real life methods of brain washing have been used to reverse a person's beliefs. Like the ideas in sci-fi, with the use of natural and mechanical methods of manipulation, what a subject sees, hears, reads, and experiences can be controlled. They can even penetrate what we might call inner conscience. Thus it was that 'messiah' Jim Jones led 900 of his followers to mass suicide at his commune in 1978.

# CYBORGS

**D**o you have any cyborgs in your family?

I'm not talking about your nan in glasses, although admittedly she is a mean combination of human and machine. Contact lenses and hearing aids don't really count either, tbh, but they do represent at least *some* level of man-machine fusion.

You see, cyborg stands for a combination of *cybernetics* and *organism*. An organism is any living thing. Whereas cybernetics is the scientific study of how humans (or aliens, animals, and machines) control and communicate information.

According to this definition, a cyborg can be anyone with a heart pacemaker, an artificial joint, an insulin pump, or a cochlear implant. So you may well have a cyborg in your midst.

And that means one of the more unlikely early examples of a cyborg in fiction is the Tin Man in Frank L Baum's 1900 classic *The Wizard of Oz*. The Tin Man was Dorothy's hero and companion on the Yellow Brick Road. The famous film adaptation of *The Wizard of Oz* was made in 1939 and the associated movie, *Oz the Great and Powerful*, in 2013.

## SO, WHAT MAKES THE TIN MAN A CYBORG?

In the original tale, he was a lumberjack called Nick Chopper (not *my* joke, for once). He was engaged to a munchkin girl named Nimmie Amee (you just can't make this stuff up; actually you *can* make it up, as he did). Anyhow, the Wicked Witch of the East conjures up a magic axe that chops off his limbs one by one (these old fairy tales are often very dark). He gradually gets them replaced with tin versions and becomes, **TA-DA! – A CYBORG**.

The book that made cyborgs famous in the US was a novel called, unsurprisingly, *Cyborg* (Americans are very straightforward people). It was written in 1972 by Martin Caidan, but most people will know it for the name of its hero, Steve Austin. Austin was a fictional test pilot who has a near-fatal air crash and has large parts of his body replaced with bionic limbs. For most of the mid-1970s Steve Austin was famous on American TV as *The Six Million Dollar Man,* a reference to how much it cost to rebuild him into a cyborg.

Boffins weren't far behind, as fact caught up with fiction. In 2000 Dr Miguel Nicolelis, a neurobiologist at the American Duke University Medical Centre, taught a monkey to use a robotic arm. The cheeky monkey's thoughts were transmitted to the arm using electrodes that were planted in the monkey's brain. This test case showed how bionic limbs could be controlled and the idea of real life cyborgs gained ground.

Like the ruthless Darth Vader and the demonic Daleks, cyborgs are among science fiction's most famous villains. Most prominent of all, however, at least in terms of being very obviously cyborgs, are the Cybermen from *Doctor Who*.

The Cybermen are a fictional race of cyborgs, a totally organic species to start with, who began to implant more and more artificial parts to help them survive. They are said to originate from Earth's twin planet Mondas (this is totally made up, btw, as we don't actually *have* a twin planet, last time we looked). As the Cybermen added more cyber parts, they became more coldly logical, calculating, and less human. As every emotion is deleted from their minds, they become less man, and more machine. You see, it's quite clever really, because you can also use the idea of Cybermen as an example of what humans may one day become if we base all our decisions on cold calculation and ignore the more human and emotional aspects. So next time you despair when asked to do some algebra, remember that you're doing the whole world a favour in helping to save us from our cybernetic future.

# INVISIBILITY

There's no doubt some things are invisible.

Sure, lots and lots of things are physical: your nan, custard, and fleas, to name but three. But just think of the things that aren't. Wind: That's invisible. (I don't mean farts, but they're invisible too.) Even though wind is part of the physical world, it can't be seen. The same is true of the kind of radiation with which you change channels on the TV. It's in the physical world (it's called infra-red radiation) but you can't see it. Not with the naked eye. IT'S INVISIBLE.

For thousands of years writers have used the idea of invisibility as a kind of plot device, something to get the story moving, something usually magical and mysterious.

Take *Doctor Faustus*, for example. This story was published in 1604 (the year before The Gunpowder Plot). *Doctor Faustus* is about a man who does a deal with the Devil himself. Sound like a bad move? Probably. But one of the magical powers he receives off old Lucifer is invisibility. What does he do with it? He goes to Rome and uses invisibility to nick the Pope's food and slap him about the head a bit.

That's the trouble with invisibility. It always seems to bring out the worst in people.

In many other legends, angels and demons were often invisible or could become so at will. In the *Mabinogi*, a set of important Welsh myths of ancient Britain, one Welsh chieftain manages to murder a bunch of others by wearing a cloak of invisibility. **SOUND FAMILIAR?**

Today's infatuation with invisibility, such as Harry Potter's version of the invisibility cloak, began with HG Wells. Old HG seems to have been involved in everything! Wells' famous novel *The Invisible Man* (1897) inspired the movie of the same name, made in 1933, along with countless comic strips and TV series about the possibility of humans being invisible.

## WHAT'S SO DIFFERENT ABOUT THE ANCIENT MYTHS AND WELLS' STORY?

HG Wells gave the idea of invisibility a scientific slant. The Invisible Man in the story is a scientist. His theory is this: if light was to move through a person in the same way it did through air, then that person might become invisible. The Invisible Man manages to do this by swallowing a potion (in those days there always seemed to be a magic chemical potion in the story somewhere). Sadly, he couldn't become visible again, which drove him bonkers.

Real-life boffins try as much as they can to avoid going mad (some are mad already). So they tend to wear invisibility cloaks, rather than swallow chemical formulas. One such cloak, developed by Professor Vladimir Shalaev at Purdue University in Indiana, is made of angled tiny metal needles that force light to pass around the cloak. The wearer appears to vanish, without the drawback of lunacy.

A working prototype is expected soon. There is one major drawback though: the current design can only bend light a bit at a time and doesn't yet work with the entire range of the visible spectrum.

## I BET THAT'S A DEVELOPMENT YOU DIDN'T SEE COMING?

# BODY PARTS

**S**ure, we all know science and medicine are working hard on human ageing. And yes, they're doing a very splendid job. Ages ago, life was nasty, brutish, and short. In the Roman Empire the average age at death was only 35. Today, the United Nations have predicted far out into the future, and by the year 2300, they say, life expectancy in most developed countries will be over 100 years. No complaints there, then.

But what if the family robot dog goes rabid? What if his circuits get a virus and he flips into 'kill' mode? Okay, you escape death, but in the brawl Fido manages to chomp off one of your arms. What then? Do you find a replacement body part?

## Frankenstein: King of the Body Parts

Almost two hundred years ago, the novel *Frankenstein* first appeared in bookshops in 1818. Written by Mary Shelley, the book famously features a creature that is entirely made up of body parts. It's a tale of a scientist called Victor Frankenstein, who becomes obsessed with making artificial life. Of course, Victor wants his creature to be beautiful, but when he builds the man out of body parts, fresh from graveyards, the result is quite grotesque. **DUH!**

Not long after *Frankenstein* scientists began to discover and dig up real monsters. The budding Industrial Revolution had unearthed the fossil record, as the great machines of the age turned over the earth. The world saw the start of dinosaur-mania and the bones and body parts of extinct monsters brought back to 'life'.

## The Body-Snatchers

About ten years after *Frankenstein*, came a real-life scandal about human body parts: the 'body snatcher' murders in Scotland. These grisly killings were committed in Edinburgh, between 1827 and 1828, by William Burke and William Hare. Burke and Hare got their victims drunk and suffocated them.

Then, they sold the still-warm corpses of their victims to Edinburgh Medical College. They killed seventeen altogether, all in the name of education. Their main customer was Professor Robert Knox, who used the corpses in the study of anatomy – a science that was blossoming at that time. You won't be surprised to hear that Edinburgh was very fearful of the body snatchers, for a while.

Over 100 years later, public horror about body parts had turned into amazement as the first heart transplant was made. In 1967 Professor Christiaan Barnard made the first successful human-to-human transplant in Capetown, South Africa.

# The Body Pirates

Also in 1967 a science fiction story predicted a future of black market body parts. The story was *The Jigsaw Man*, by Larry Niven. In the tale Larry invented the fictional crime of organlegging, meaning the piracy and smuggling of organs! The story imagines a future where the transplant of any organ is possible, and life can potentially be extended forever. But when the death rate goes down, the number of donors decreases. They need these fictional body snatchers to keep the system going!

Back in the real world the BBC reported factual organlegging in 2006. The sale of organs taken from executed death row inmates was thriving in China. One hospital said it could provide a liver at a cost of £50,000.

A very recent body-parts story is *Spares* by Michael Marshall Smith. The book was written in 1996 and foresees a future where 'Farms' of clones (spares) are kept as an insurance policy for the rich and powerful. Lost an eye, limb, or organ? No problem. Money talks. The body part is taken from your clone, and you get your replacement. **VERY GRISLY.**

The future foreseen in *Spares* is very similar to the 2005 movie *The Island*. It is 2019 and most of the outside world has been contaminated. A community of people rescued from the toxic environment believe they are living in a perfect, but isolated, colony. The reality is sinister, however; the colonists are actually clones. They are walking and talking spares, and their sole purpose is to provide medical insurance for their celebrity sponsors.

# TOP 10
## MUTANTS / X-MEN

*Our reading campaign continues with a look at our Top Ten Mutants. Once again, get studying!*

## 1 Wolverine

*First Appearance:* Incredible Hulk *No. 180, 1974*
*Mutant Power: Speedy healing factor*

**MUTANT MERITS:** a complex character behind his raging temper and ferocious claws, Wolverine features in the coolest X-Men stories, from the Canadian wilderness to the back streets of Japan. His rivalry with Cyclops, his close friendships with Nightcrawler and Jean Grey, and his mentoring of Kitty Pryde makes Wolverine the centre of the X-Men universe.

## 2 Cyclops

*First Appearance:* X-Men *No. 1, 1963*
*Mutant Power: Optic blasts*

**MUTANT MERITS:** the keenest recruit in Professor X's dream of peace between mutants and humans, Cyclops is a key part of the X-Men world.

# 3  Storm

*First Appearance:* Giant Size X-Men *No. 1, 1975*
*Mutant Power: Weather control*

**MUTANT MERITS:** she's changed from thief to goddess to warrior to queen; few X-Men have evolved over the years as much as Storm. One of the strongest female characters, not just in the history of the X-Men, but in all comics. The X-Men experienced perhaps their best years with Storm as leader.

# 4  Nightcrawler

*First Appearance:* Giant Size X-Men *No. 1, 1975*
*Mutant Power: Teleportation*

**MUTANT MERITS:** the most alien-looking mutant in the X-Men, Nightcrawler is dramatic and funny which makes him one of the most likable X-Men. As one fan said, "a study in extremes, Nightcrawler can bring a smile to your face or a tear to your eye."

# 5  Professor X

*First Appearance:* X-Men *No. 1, 1963*
*Mutant Power: Telepathy*

**MUTANT MERITS:** Professor Charles Xavier's dream of

peace between humans and mutants is the main story behind the entire X-Men series. Even though he set up the X-Men, Professor X is not loved by everyone. Some see him as a saintly father figure, others see him as a man willing to endanger the lives of children to make his dream come true.

# 6 Jean Grey

*First Appearance:* X-Men *No. 1, 1963*
*Mutant Power: Telepathy, Telekinesis, and Phoenix Force*

MUTANT MERITS: perhaps the best of all X-Men stories is the tale of Jean Grey learning how to use her powers without being tempted to become too much like a god!

# 7 Colossus

*First Appearance:* Giant Size X-Men *No. 1, 1975*
*Mutant Power: Transforms into organic steel*

MUTANT MERITS: one of the strongest X-Men, Colossus is also gentle and kind. Colossus has survived the sadness of losing his family and becomes stronger, with a heart as unbreakable as his steel skin.

# 8 Cable

*First Appearance:* Uncanny X-Men *No. 201, 1986*
*Mutant Power: Telepathy, Telekinesis*

**MUTANT MERITS**: one of the more complicated mutants in the X-Men universe, Cable is at first a mysterious soldier from the future. But then he has a child to look after, which makes him softer and more important to the future of mutantkind.

# 9 Emma Frost

*First Appearance:* X-Men *No. 129, 1980*
*Mutant Power: Telepathy, Diamond form*

**MUTANT MERITS**: one of the most unpredictable X-Men, you never know what to expect of Emma Frost. At any moment she may adopt her ice queen exterior, or even something more sinister.

# 10 Kitty Pryde

*First Appearance:* X-Men *No. 129, 1980*
*Mutant Power: Quantum tunnelling*

**MUTANT MERITS**: Kitty Pryde first came into the X-Men team in the early '80s, with explosive results. Though Kitty has changed into a woman of great power, she is still the entry point to the X-Men for many readers.

# TOP 10 VILLAINS

*Who are the greatest villains in the history of science fiction? And are these villains born bad or has fate dealt them a poor hand breeding villainy in their blood?* **MWAHAHAHAHAHAHAH!**

## 1 Darth Vader

*Claim to fame: the darthest dad in the* Star Wars *universe.*

**BORN OR BRED:** old Darth had very little screen time in the first *Star Wars* movie, but he totally stole the show. His villainous credentials include: the fact he is part machine, his use of the dark side, and his breathy, rasping – and much imitated – voice. Darth was so impressive that the entire *Star Wars* prequel trilogy was about him. We found that he wasn't *born* bad, but instead he was a victim of events. **VILLAINOUS FACT:** the American Film Institute voted Darth the third greatest movie villain of all time.

## 2 Agent Smith

*Claim to fame: another show-stealer, this time from The Matrix franchise.*

**BORN OR BRED:** hmm, tricky. Agent Smith is actually an AI computer program created to keep order in the system, so we could easily argue he's born bad. Having said that, he also evolves in the story, making copies of himself and getting more villainous by inserting himself into the real world, so he's a little bit bred too. He wore glasses to improve his websight (geddit?!)

# 3  The Daleks

*Claim to fame: extraterrestrial alien race of mutants in* Doctor Who.

**BORN OR BRED**: their atrocities are legion, but their history is interesting. The Daleks are a genetically modified race of aliens (the Kaleds from the planet Skaro) whose ability to feel pity and compassion was removed by their chief egghead, Davros. So, he's the psycho, not the Daleks! But let's not invite them to tea just yet...

# 4  The Joker

*Claim to fame: highly intelligent master criminal and Batman's nemesis in* The Dark Knight.

**BORN OR BRED**: pretty impressive in the scary stakes. The Joker is able to tell tall tales (why so serious?), as well as being something of a chillingly sane psycho. He may have had a rough childhood, but like all psychopaths, he was pretty much **BORN** that way!

## 5 Khan

*Claim to fame: the brilliant villain from* Star Trek: Into Darkness, *who once controlled more than one quarter of the Earth.*

**BORN OR BRED:** not only brilliant, but charming, fearless, ruthless, and a master of manipulation. The only thing that stops him being a full-out pyscho is his fierce loyalty to his crew (witness that great Khan quote, "After every single person aboard your ship suffocates, I will walk over your cold corpses to recover my people"). **BRED.**

## 6 Loki

*Claim to fame: brother to Thor in mythology and in the* Thor *movies.*

**BORN OR BRED:** hmm, is Loki a born psycho or does he just have daddy issues? How would any of us react to learning our dad was actually a Frost Giant from the world of Jotunheim? Having said that, in the comics he is also called 'God of Lies and Mischief and God of Evil'. That doesn't look good. **BORN PSYCHO.**

## 7 Magneto

*Claim to fame: the primary villain of the* X-Men *franchise.*

**BORN OR BRED:** a merciless mass murderer, prepared to kill all humans as the only way to prevent them from killing all mutants. A rather extreme policy. No matter how you've been treated in life (and Magneto *did* spend years at the hands of the Nazis), such insane ideas suggest a born PSYCHO.

## 8  Terminator T-1000

*Claim to fame: the shape-shifting robotic assassin from* Terminator II.

BORN OR BRED: a shifty villain made of liquid metal who's able to change into other objects or people of equal mass. Cool trick for a villain. He can even pretend to be a floor! And don't think he's *bound* to be a born psycho just because he's programmed that way. Aren't human psychos also programmed by their genes? BRED.

## 9  General Zod

*Claim to fame: the supervillain and military Kryptonian from the* Superman *franchise.*

BORN OR BRED: tricky. In the original 1980 *Superman* film, Zod was no doubt a psycho, threatening that all Earthlings would pay for protecting Superman. But in *Man of Steel* (2013), it turns out Zod was once a loyal military leader, so the answer is both!

# 10 The Master

*Claim to fame: Time Lord archenemy of the Doctor.*

**BORN OR BRED:** someone whose aims include 'wanting to control the universe' and wanting to be 'master of all matter' clearly has issues, but the Master wasn't born that way. We found that, as a lad on Gallifrey, he had stared into a time vortex (whatever *that* is), which by all accounts drives you insane. **BRED.**

# TOP 10 MAD DOCTORS

*Modern science provides us with plenty of monsters, doesn't it? The Bomb. The killer computer. The deadly strain. The genetically modified android-teacher. But who are the Top 10 Mad Doctors of science from film and fiction?*

## 1 Dr Frankenstein

*Claim to fame: the first great myth of the modern age; the original and still the maddest.*

Frankenstein was, of course, the name of the scientist, not the creature.

**MAD PEDIGREE:** the full title of Mary Shelley's 1818 novel is *Frankenstein; or, The Modern Prometheus.* It reminds us of Prometheus, who stole fire from the gods for humanity's profit. And that's what Victor Frankenstein dreamed about: unlimited power through science. Scientist as god, creates life, goes gaga.

## 2 Dr Strangelove

*Claim to fame: the most influential mad doctor of the movies.*

**MAD PEDIGREE:** he is mad, in the custom of Victor

Frankenstein, and he is part robotic, implying Dalek-like inhumanity. His black-gloved arm forever jerks out into a Sieg Heil with embarrassing zeal. As the man who played Strangelove put it, "the arm hated the rest of the body for having made a compromise – that arm was a Nazi."

## 3 Dr Rotwang

*Claim to fame: from the 1927 film,* Metropolis, *and one of the very early examples of the mad doctor.*

MAD PEDIGREE: he created the first female robota *Maschinenmensch,* had a wild, unkempt shock of Einsteinesque hair and a lab to die for (or in).

## 4 Dr Emmett L Brown

*Claim to fame: from the* Back to the Future *series of films, inventor of the coolest time machine of all.*

MAD PEDIGREE: wild eyes, crazy Einstein hair (again), madcap mannerisms, he threw his family fortune into inventions such as a mind reading device, robot breakfast makers, and, to be fair, that very cool car that travels in time.

## 5 Dr Jekyll

*Claim to fame: from the 1886 novel* The Strange Case of Dr Jekyll and Mr Hyde. *The very phrase 'Jekyll and Hyde' has come to mean wild or bipolar behaviour.*

**MAD PEDIGREE:** on supping a chemical mixture, Dr Jekyll is transformed from a sensible scientist into the raving loony Mr Hyde. **POTION, ANYONE?**

# 6 Dr Otto Octavious (Doc Ock)

*Claim to fame: from the movie* Spiderman II, *Doc Ock, or Doctor Octopus, turns to crime to feed his ever-madder inventions.*

**MAD PEDIGREE:** a normal genius-level boffin who creates a nuclear powered mechanical octopus suit that goes haywire. Hey, come on, that could happen to anyone...

# 7 Dr No

*Claim to fame: Dr Julius No, the very first* James Bond *movie villain, a 'brilliant' scientist and an "unwanted child of a German missionary and a Chinese girl of a good family".* **UH OH.**

**MAD PEDIGREE:** An atomic scientist who, like Strangelove and Rotwang, wears sinister black leather gloves. Note: if you're ever watching a movie and a boffin with black gloves comes on? He is **ALWAYS** a baddie.

# 8 Dr Evil

*Claim to fame: the demonic doctor from the* Austin Powers *series of movies.*

**MAD PEDIGREE:** a bald-headed, cat-loving supervillain (be honest, he sounds weird already) and bent on world domination. Of course. Best invention? Sharks with laser beams tied to their heads. **AWESOME.**

# 9  Dr Hannibal Lector

*Claim to fame: in 2003, the American Film Institute named him the number one movie villain of all time.*

**MAD PEDIGREE:** an ingenious, cultured Lithuanian shrink and serial killer, who eats his victims, with a little wine. **ENOUGH SAID.**

# 10  Dr Bruce Banner

*Claim to fame: the scientist behind the identity of* The Incredible Hulk *and considered to be a top scientific mind.*

**MAD PEDIGREE:** after being exposed to gamma radiation in an experiment gone wrong, Banner turns into the angry green monster known as The Hulk every time he gets mad. On the plus side, that also makes him a part-time superhero as one of The Avengers.

## DOCTOR WHO EDITION

Bulging with mind-bending stories, characters, and science concepts that have excited and educated *Doctor Who* fans over the last half a century. And, for an extra bit of fun, our very own *Doctor Who* Top 10s, on topics such as aliens, androids, companions, and catchphrases!

*Available from Candy Jar Books*

## TOMMY PARKER: DESTINY WILL FIND YOU
by Anthony Ormond

When Tommy Parker packs his bag and goes to his grandpa's house for the summer he has no idea that his life is about to change forever.

But that's exactly what happens when his grandpa lets him in on a fantastic secret: he has a pen that lets him travel through his own memories and alter the past. Imagine that! Being able to travel into your own past and re-write your history.

*Tommy Parker: Destiny Will Find You!* is an exhilarating adventure that redefines the time travel genre.

You'll never look at your memories in quite the same way again…

ISBN: 978-0-9928607-1-4

*Also available from Candy Jar Books*

**LETHBRIDGE-STEWART: THE FORGOTTEN SON**
by Andy Frankham-Allen

For Colonel Alistair Lethbridge-Stewart his life in the Scots Guards was straightforward enough; rising in the ranks through nineteen years of military service. But then his regiment was assigned to help combat the Yeti incursion in London, the robotic soldiers of an alien entity known as the Great Intelligence. For Lethbridge-Stewart, life would never be the same again.

Meanwhile in the small Cornish village of Bledoe a man is haunted by the memory of an accident thirty years old. The Hollow Man of Remington Manor seems to have woken once more. And in Coleshill, Buckinghamshire, Mary Gore is plagued by the voice of a small boy, calling her home.

What connects these strange events to the recent Yeti incursion, and just what has it all to do with Lethbridge-Stewart?

A brand-new series of novels set just after the *Doctor Who* serial *The Web of Fear*, featuring the characters and concepts created by Mervyn Haisman & Henry Lincoln.

ISBN: 978-0-9931191-5-6